Dear Reader,

Sadness touches all of our lives at different times, but depression can have enormous depths and staying power that reach beyond those of simple sadness. Feeling hopeless, worthless, or just empty and numb are classic signs of depression. You may find it difficult to concentrate, make decisions, or enjoy things that used to bring you pleasure. You may notice that you are sleeping or eating either too much or too little, or that you have fatigue, headaches, or aches and pains that seem to have sprung up without a cause. You are not alone. Fully one in six adults suffers from depression at some point.

If you've ever been diagnosed with depression or been close to someone who has, you know that this illness cannot be wished away. A person in the grip of depression can't solve his or her problems by showing a little more backbone or by simply shaking off the blues. Yet too many people struggle silently. A 2017 survey from the National Survey on Drug Use and Health found that among adults with a major depressive episode, about one in three received no treatment.

Medications and therapy can help. One study showed that, for those who stuck with treatment, depression lifted completely in seven out of 10 people. For many others, treatment relieves many, though not all, symptoms. Effective treatment can lighten your mood, strengthen your connections with loved ones, allow you to find satisfaction in interests and hobbies, and make you feel more like yourself again. In 2019, two new depression drugs were approved by the FDA, including one for postpartum depression and the other a fast-acting nasal spray for hard-to-treat cases.

To find the right treatment, you may need patience and perseverance—which can be a tall order when you are feeling depressed. Some people immediately hit upon a medication or therapy that works for them. But for many others, the treatment path takes several turns and an occasional detour. You may need to adjust medications, alter a dosage, or try a new therapist. Side effects, health insurance coverage, and the stigma associated with having a mood problem can make getting help more difficult. The advice in this report should help you get the treatment you need. We also offer self-care strategies and complementary therapies that can enhance your mood.

Today's scientific findings are paving the way for better treatment. Genetic discoveries and brain imaging techniques are helping doctors better understand the biology of depression, which may one day make more targeted, personalized treatment possible. In the meantime, we hope that this report helps you work with your doctor to find a treatment that restores your sense of well-being and makes more room for joy in your life.

Sincerely,

Michael Craig Miller, M.D.
Medical Editor

Harvard Health Publishing | Harvard Medical School | 4 Blackfan Circle, 4th Floor | Boston, MA 02115

What is depression?

People tend to use the term depression loosely. For instance, you might sigh, "I'm so depressed!" after a rough patch at work or when a favorite sports team loses a game. But to a doctor who treats depression, such examples would likely be seen as normal fluctuations in mood. What about a more serious personal loss, such as losing a job or ending a relationship? The deeper pain of grief would be a common response—for a while. But what if those blue feelings linger, leaving you unmotivated, listless, or irritable? How do you know when the problem has gotten intense enough that you should see a professional?

If you're even asking the question, it's time to seek help. Depression isn't a one-size-fits-all illness. Just like cancer or heart disease, depression can take many forms. This report addresses three main categories: major depressive disorder (also called major depression), persistent depressive disorder, and bipolar disorder. Together, these conditions affect roughly one in 10 American adults. Each has its distinguishing features, but symptoms overlap, and all involve periods of low mood that can compromise functioning or well-being. Yet even within each category, people's experiences vary.

Whichever type of depression you suspect you have, do not struggle in silence. Depression or hopelessness may feel so paralyzing that you find it hard to seek help. Even worse, you may believe that treatment could never overcome the heavy weight bearing down on you. Yet nothing could be further from the truth. The vast majority of people who receive proper treatment for major depression, for example, rebound in a relatively short period of time and take pleasure in life once again.

Even if your symptoms are vague and even if they don't necessarily match the criteria for depressive disorders described in this chapter, you may still benefit from a doctor's opinion and evaluation. If you feel lost or stuck, or are concerned about a feeling, thought, behavior, or situation, seek help. This report will give you the resources you need to get the proper treatment. It may be that you need to try a combination of therapies to get the best results. Again, this report will help you sort through your options. But first, you need to understand the three main types of depression.

Many people believe that treatment could never overcome the weight of depression bearing down on them. But the vast majority of people who receive proper treatment find relief.

Major depressive disorder

Major depressive disorder, by definition, is depression in its classic form. You may feel as though work, school, relationships, and other aspects of your life have been derailed or put on hold indefinitely. You feel constantly sad or burdened, or you lose interest in all activities, even those you previously enjoyed.

The symptoms are described in the *Diagnostic and Statistical Manual of Mental Disorders*, which formally classifies psychiatric disorders for clinicians and researchers. (The current, fifth edition of the book, commonly known as the *DSM-5*, was published in May 2013.) According to this manual, the defining symptoms of depression should be present nearly all day, on most days, and for at least two weeks, in order to qualify for a formal diagnosis. But don't focus too much on the two-week criterion, as it may be hard to pinpoint exactly when your symptoms began. If you're wondering if you're depressed, call your doctor.

A diagnosis of major depressive disorder is made if a person experiences at least five of the following nine symptoms (and at least one of them must be either the first or second symptom listed here):

- depressed mood most of the day, nearly every day
- loss of interest or pleasure in most or all activities
- change in appetite or weight
- trouble sleeping, or sleeping too much
- sluggish thinking and movement, or restlessness and agitation
- low energy
- thoughts of worthlessness or guilt
- poor concentration
- recurrent thoughts about death or suicide.

People with depression are likely to have anxiety as well, so you may also feel worried or distressed more often than you used to. Other signs can include pessimism or hopelessness, a loss of sexual desire, and physical symptoms such as headaches, unexplained aches and pains, or digestive problems.

Although these symptoms are hallmarks of depression, if you talk to any two depressed people about their experiences, you might think they were describing entirely different illnesses. For example, one might not be able to muster the energy to leave the house, while the other might feel agitated and restless. One might feel deeply sad and break into tears easily. The other might snap irritably at the least provocation. One picks at food, while the other eats constantly. The two people might both say they feel sad, but the quality of their moods could be very different in depth and darkness. Also, symptoms may gather over a period of days, weeks, or months.

Hopelessness can make it hard to seek help. You may feel unmotivated or may not believe that treatment will make a difference. But that's simply not true. Most people who receive proper treatment rebound emotionally within four to six weeks and then take pleasure in life once again. By contrast, when major depression goes untreated, it can last for months or years.

If you are having suicidal thoughts

Seek help immediately. The National Suicide Prevention Lifeline has a hotline that is free and available 24 hours a day. Call 800-273-TALK (800-273-8255), and you'll be connected to a skilled, trained counselor at a crisis center in your area. Alternatively, you can call 911 or go to your local emergency room. (For more information about suicide, see "Suicide: Understanding the risk," page 47.)

What's more, episodes of depression frequently recur. About half of those who sink into an episode of major depression will have at least one more episode later in life. Some researchers think that diagnosing depression early and treating it successfully can help forestall such recurrences. They suspect that the more episodes of depression you've had, the more likely you are to have future episodes, because depression may cause lasting changes in brain circuits and chemicals that affect mood (see "The problem of recurrence," page 15). In addition, people who suffer from recurrent major depression have a higher risk of developing bipolar disorder than people who experience a single episode.

Persistent depressive disorder

Until 2013, persistent depressive disorder was known as dysthymic disorder, or dysthymia (dis-THIGH-me-ah) for short. The condition is characterized by a low-level drone of depression that lasts for at least two years in adults or one year in children and teens. While not necessarily as crippling as major depression, its persistent hold can keep you from feeling good and can intrude upon your work, school, and social life. If you think of depression as the color black, persistent depressive disorder is more like a dim gray. Unlike major depression, in which relatively short episodes may be separated by long stretches of stability, persistent depressive disorder lasts an average of five years.

If you suffer from persistent depressive disorder, more often than not you feel depressed during most of the day. You may be able to deal with everyday life, but

Mild, moderate, or severe depression?

Experts judge the severity of depression by assessing the number of symptoms and the degree to which they impair your life.

Mild: You have some symptoms and find it takes more effort than usual to accomplish what you need to do.

Moderate: You have many symptoms and find they often keep you from accomplishing what you need to do.

Severe: You have nearly all the symptoms and find they almost always keep you from accomplishing daily tasks.

much of the zest is gone. Your depressed mood doesn't lift for more than two months at a time, and you also have at least two of the following symptoms:

- overeating or loss of appetite
- insomnia or sleeping too much
- tiredness or lack of energy
- low self-esteem
- trouble concentrating or making decisions
- hopelessness.

Persistent depressive disorder often begins in childhood, the teen years, or early adulthood. Being drawn into this low-level depression makes major depression more likely. In fact, there is a great deal of overlap between these two forms of depression—the majority of people who are diagnosed with persistent depressive disorder will have an episode of major depression within five years. When major depressive disorder is added to persistent depressive disorder, it is sometimes called "double depression."

Although the symptoms of persistent depressive disorder may appear milder than major depression, suffering can be significant over time. Only about 10% of people get better on their own in a given year, and then relapse is common without treatment. Treatment eases symptoms in about four out of five people.

Bipolar disorder

Some people with depression also experience periods when they feel unusually active and energetic, or manic. These mood swings are the hallmark of bipolar disorder. In the most common form, called bipolar I disorder, a person has one or more manic episodes—periods of a week or longer where mood is terrifically elated, expansive, or irritable, plus at least three of the following symptoms:

- grandiose ideas or pumped-up self-esteem
- far less need for sleep than normal
- a pressing urge to talk
- racing thoughts
- distractibility
- increased activity or agitation
- pleasure-seeking without regard to negative consequences.

Sometimes, manic episodes can be so severe that hospitalization is necessary to prevent harmful outcomes. Between episodes, for months or years, a person might feel completely normal.

Bipolar disorder takes many forms. Cycles of mood episodes can be infrequent or very frequent. Intensity of episodes can also vary.

One common variant is called bipolar II disorder. In this pattern, a person has episodes of depression along with milder episodes of elated mood called hypomania. "Hypo" means "less than," so hypomania is less intense than mania. During a hypomanic episode, you might feel energized, happy, and productive. And while you don't feel that anything is wrong, your family and friends may notice your mood is elevated beyond the usual. Be sure to tell your doctor, because getting the right treatment is important, as hypomania may be a sign that a manic or depressive episode is coming.

Bipolar disorder usually starts in the late teens or early adulthood. It's equally common among women and men, although hypomania occurs more often in women. Women are also more likely to experience major depression as their first episode and to have more depressive episodes over all. Men, on the other hand, typically experience manic episodes first and tend to have more of them than depressive cycles.

Bipolar disorder is a persistent illness. Nine out of 10 people who have one manic episode can expect to have another. But successful treatment can cut down on the number and intensity of episodes and reduce suicide risk.

Causes of depression

Your mood, your perceptions, and the way you experience life all arise from within your brain. Therefore, delving into the causes of depression requires studying the brain. Yet the brain is so complicated, scientists are still just beginning to understand this ever-changing, dynamic organ. Some things are clear, however.

Myriad factors can affect your brain—beginning before you're even born and continuing throughout your lifetime. Some of these factors involve nature (your genetic makeup and your brain functioning) and some involve nurture (all the environmental influences you experience). These interact to cause mood problems. Either can alter your brain chemistry and may even cause subtle changes in your brain structure.

Neurotransmitters involved in depression

Acetylcholine enhances memory and is involved in learning and recall.

Dopamine helps regulate movement and emotional responses. Because it is part of the brain's reward system, dopamine is thought to play a role in substance use disorders.

Gamma-aminobutyric acid (GABA) is an amino acid that's thought to help quell anxiety.

Glutamate appears to be involved in bipolar disorder and schizophrenia. Lithium carbonate, a well-known mood stabilizer used to treat bipolar disorder, helps prevent damage to neurons in the brains of rats exposed to high levels of glutamate.

Norepinephrine constricts blood vessels, raising blood pressure. It may trigger anxiety and be involved in some types of depression. It also seems to help determine motivation and reward.

Serotonin helps regulate sleep, appetite, and mood and inhibits pain. Some depressed people have reduced serotonin transmission. Low levels of a serotonin byproduct have been linked to a higher risk for suicide.

Certain areas of the brain in particular help regulate mood and are involved in depression (see Figure 1, page 6). The ways in which your brain cells (specifically, nerve cells, or neurons) grow, connect to each other, and function also affect your mood. Neurons communicate through chemical messengers called neurotransmitters (see "Neurotransmitters involved in depression," below left). Genes make proteins that are involved in all the biological processes in your body, including the production and breakdown of neurotransmitters. But depression is far more complex than an imbalance of neurotransmitters, as you will see in this chapter.

Environmental factors are also influential. For example, you might be exposed to a toxic substance—or have a "toxic" encounter with another person. A toxic substance could be a drug (illegal or prescription), and a toxic encounter could be an episode of verbal or physical abuse. Each of us enters life with unique genetic predispositions, and we are all exposed over time to a range of stressors, both physical and emotional. These differences help explain why depression takes many different forms. But even if two people have similar symptoms of depression, the underlying problem—and therefore what treatments will work best—may be entirely different.

Following are major factors thought to play a role in depression.

Stressful life events

Stress is an inevitable part of life. Someone close to you dies, you lose your job or become seriously ill, or a relationship falls apart—these are the types of events that often trigger depression and prompt a person to seek help. In addition, some people must cope with longstanding or extreme stressors, such as the early loss of a parent, violence, or sexual abuse. While not everyone who faces these stresses develops a mood disorder—in fact, most do not—stress plays an important role in depression. Even minor stressors can play a role if you have an unrelenting stream of them (see "Does social media lift you up—or bring you down?" on page 7).

Stress triggers a chain of chemical reactions and responses in the body. If the stress is short-lived, the body usually returns to normal. But when stress is chronic or the system gets stuck in overdrive, changes in the body and brain can be long-lasting.

How stress affects the body

Stress can be defined as your body's automatic physical response to an outside stimulus that requires you to adjust to change. Every real or perceived threat to your body triggers a cascade of stress hormones that produces physiological changes. We all know the sensations: your heart pounds, muscles tense, breathing quickens, and beads of sweat appear. This is known as the stress response. The stress response starts with a signal from the part of your brain known as the hypothalamus.

When a physical or emotional threat looms, the hypothalamus boosts production of corticotropin-releasing hormone (CRH). Hormones are complex chemicals that carry messages to organs or groups of cells throughout the body and trigger certain responses. Through a series of hormone sig-

Figure 1: Areas of the brain involved with depression

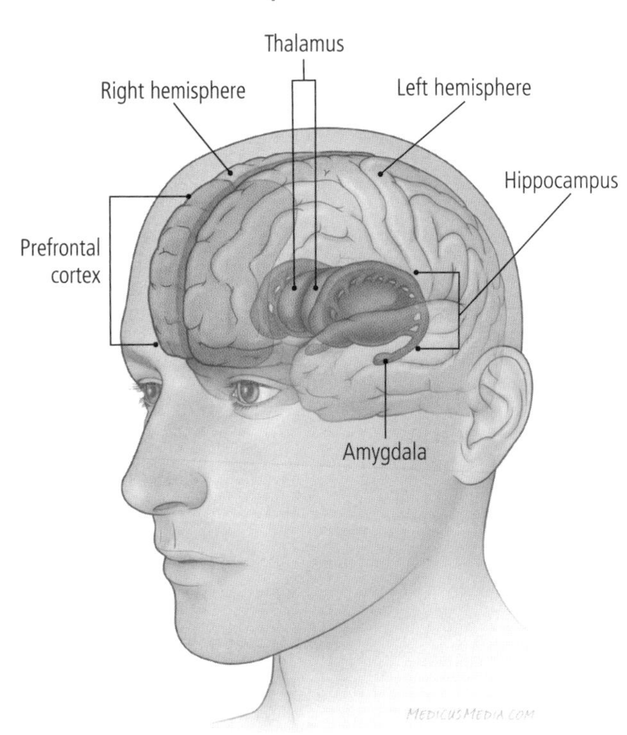

The regions shown here are mirrored in both hemispheres of the brain. Also, these structures are interlocking; the illustration suggests relative position but not precise location.

Amygdala: The amygdala is part of a group of structures deep in the brain that's associated with emotions such as anger, pleasure, sorrow, fear, and sexual arousal. Recalling an emotionally charged memory, such as a frightening situation, activates the amygdala. Activity in the amygdala is higher when a person is sad or clinically depressed, and this continues even after recovery from depression. This increase in activity may actually cause the amygdala to enlarge.

Basal ganglia (not pictured): The basal ganglia are a related group of structures deep in the brain. They are connected to and interact with structures that are closer to the brain's surface. They may help facilitate movement and may be involved in memorizing, thinking, and emotional processing. Some studies have found shrinkage and other structural changes in the basal ganglia in people with depression.

Hippocampus: The hippocampus plays a key role in processing long-term memory. Interplay between the hippocampus and the amygdala might account for the adage "once bitten, twice shy." It is this part of the brain that registers fear when you are confronted by a barking, aggressive dog, and the memory of such an experience may make you wary of dogs you come across later in life. The hippocampus is smaller in some depressed people, and research suggests that ongoing exposure to stress hormones impairs the growth of neurons in this part of the brain.

Insula: Tucked into a fold of the brain (and therefore not shown here), this part of the brain is involved in processing emotions and psychological self-awareness, a feeling that you can make changes to improve your life.

Prefrontal cortex: Found in the frontmost part of the brain, this region is believed to play a role in complex reasoning, decision making, the expression of personality, and social behavior. Some studies have found changes in the structure of the prefrontal cortex among people with depression.

Thalamus: The thalamus receives most sensory information and relays it to brain structures that direct high-level functions such as speech, behavioral reactions, movement, thinking, and learning. Some research suggests that bipolar disorder may involve problems in the thalamus, which helps link sensory input to pleasant and unpleasant feelings.

nals involving the adrenal and pituitary glands, CRH prompts the adrenal glands to release cortisol, which readies your body to fight or flee. Your heart beats faster and your blood pressure rises. Your breath quickens as your body takes in extra oxygen. Sharpened senses, such as sight and hearing, make you more alert.

CRH also affects the parts of the brain that manage mood (see Figure 1, page 6). It is thought to play a major role in coordinating your thoughts and behaviors, emotional reactions, and involuntary responses. Working along a variety of neural pathways, CRH influences the concentration of neurotransmitters throughout the brain (see "Neurotransmitters involved in depression," page 5). Disturbances in hormonal systems, therefore, may well affect neurotransmitters, and vice versa.

Normally, a feedback loop allows the body to turn off "fight-or-flight" defenses when the threat passes. In some cases, though, the floodgates never close properly, and cortisol levels rise too often or simply stay high. This can contribute to problems such as high blood pressure, immune suppression, asthma, and possibly depression.

People who are depressed typically have higher-than-normal levels of CRH. Antidepressants and electroconvulsive therapy are both known to reduce these high CRH levels. As CRH levels return to normal, depressive symptoms recede. But there are ways to help calm the stress response. For one example, see "Mindfulness meditation," page 44.

Losses and trauma

Certain events can have lasting physical, as well as emotional, consequences. People who suffer loss or trauma during childhood—such as neglect, the death of a parent, or sexual or physical abuse—have a higher risk of developing depression than those who haven't faced such hardships. Evidence points to a clear link between childhood trauma and increased levels of stress hormones, as well as changes in gene regulation and even brain structure. These may account for the development of depression.

Not surprisingly, loneliness and isolation also leave people more vulnerable to depression. Paradoxically, too much time spent on social media can make you feel more lonely rather than less (see "Does social media lift you up—or bring you down?" below left). Strains in family and marital relationships, or persistent troubles in any important relationship (quarreling, negative attitudes or behaviors) in any important relationship have a similar impact.

Does social media lift you up—or bring you down?

Facebook, Instagram, and other social media apps can help people stay in touch with friends and colleagues and keep track of social events, news, and other trends. But these platforms often cause people to compare their lives with others, which can create feelings of missing out, loneliness, or low mood.

A 2018 study of undergraduates at the University of Pennsylvania found that students who limited their use of Facebook, Instagram, and Snapchat to 30 minutes a day for three weeks reported much less loneliness and depression compared with a control group that made no changes to their social media diet. Be mindful of how and how much you use social media and what role it plays it your life. If you spend large chunks of time scrolling through these platforms, try cutting back and perhaps replacing that time with healthier activities, such as visiting with friends, walking in nature, or pursuing a creative hobby.

Medical problems

Certain medical problems are linked to lasting, significant mood disturbances. In fact, medical illnesses or medications may be at the root of up to 10% to 15% of all depression cases (see "Depression as a side effect of medication," page 8).

Among the best-known culprits are two thyroid hormone imbalances. Too much thyroid hormone (hyperthyroidism) can trigger manic symptoms. On the other hand, too little thyroid hormone (hypothyroidism) often leads to exhaustion and depression. Nutritional deficiencies, such as a lack of vitamin B_{12}, can also cause depressive symptoms; a B_{12} deficiency is more likely to occur in older adults.

Heart disease has also been linked to depression, with up to half of heart attack survivors reporting

Depression as a side effect of medication

Sometimes, symptoms of depression or mania are a side effect of certain drugs. Some of these drugs cause symptoms like malaise (a general feeling of being ill or uncomfortable) or appetite loss that may be mistaken for depression. Other drugs with sedating effects tend to lower your energy level and may, in turn, dampen your mood. And sometimes, medications are blamed for depression when the symptoms may actually stem from the illness for which the drug was prescribed (such as cancer or heart disease).

The clearest links are from two main classes of drugs: glucocorticoids and interferons. Glucocorticoids (also referred to as steroids) are used to treat many conditions, including autoimmune diseases, allergies, asthma, and some forms of cancer. Examples include prednisone and methylprednisolone (Medrol, others). Interferons are used to treat viral infections and various cancers; examples include interferon beta-1a (Avonex) and interferon beta-1b (Betaseron).

Be sure to tell your doctor or therapist what medications you take and when your symptoms began. A professional can help sort out whether a new medication, a change in dosage, or interactions with other drugs or substances might be causing your problems.

feeling blue and many having significant depression. Depression can spell trouble for people with heart disease; it's been linked with slower recovery, future heart trouble, and a higher risk of dying within about six months.

The following medical conditions have also been associated with mood disorders:

- multiple sclerosis, Parkinson's disease, Alzheimer's disease, Huntington's disease, and related ailments
- stroke
- hormone imbalances caused by problems with the parathyroid or adrenal glands
- certain immune system diseases, such as lupus
- some viruses and other infections, such as mononucleosis, hepatitis, and HIV
- cancer
- erectile dysfunction in men.

Sometimes, it's hard to tell which came first—the medical condition or the mood changes. Certainly, the stress of a life-threatening or serious illness such as cancer can trigger depression. In other cases, depression precedes the medical illness and may even contribute to it. To find out whether the mood changes occurred on their own or as a result of the medical illness, a doctor carefully considers a person's medical history and the results of a physical exam.

If depression or mania springs from an underlying medical problem, the mood changes should disappear after the medical condition is treated. If you have hypothyroidism, for example, lethargy and low mood may lift once treatment regulates the level of thyroid hormone in your blood.

When a person has a vulnerability to depression, the episode may be triggered by the medical illness, but the depression is an independent problem. In those cases, in order to be successful, treatment must address depression directly.

Changes in brain function

The brain usually functions well enough to keep mood, learning, movement, and senses perking along. But in some people who are depressed or manic, any of the complex systems that handle these functions may go awry. That is, the processes inside cells, the interactions between neurotransmitters and receptors, or the communication between brain regions can become overactive or underresponsive.

Increasingly sophisticated forms of brain imaging permit a much closer look at the working brain than was possible in the past. Certain types of brain scans, for example, can track changes that take place when a region of the brain responds during various tasks. Other types of scans can map the brain by measuring the distribution and density of receptors for brain chemicals in certain areas.

These studies have enabled scientists to identify and study the areas of the brain that appear to play a role in depression. One notable structure, the hippocampus (see Figure 1, page 6), is involved in learning, memory, and emotion. In some people with depression, it is smaller than normal. Stress, which plays a role in depression, might explain this difference, since animal studies show that stress can suppress neurogenesis (the growth of new neurons) in the hippocampus.

Seasonal affective disorder: When winter brings the blues

Many people feel sad when summer wanes, but some actually develop depression with the season's change. Known as seasonal affective disorder (SAD), this form of depression affects about 1% to 2% of the population, particularly women and young people. Risk increases as you move farther from the equator; for example, rates are just 1% in Florida but 9% in Alaska and New England.

SAD seems to be triggered by a drop in daily sunlight exposure. It usually comes on during the fall or winter months and subsides in the spring. Symptoms are similar to other forms of depression.

Experts don't yet understand what causes SAD. They believe that the cause may lie in how the length of the day affects complex systems governing the body clock, the hormone melatonin, and the chemical messenger serotonin. All three are influenced in complicated ways by fluctuations in the daily duration of daylight.

Treatments for SAD include medications and cognitive behavioral therapy, as well as light therapy (also called phototherapy). Light therapy involves daily sessions of sitting close to a special light source that is far more intense than normal indoor light. Experts typically recommend 30 minutes of daily exposure first thing in the morning. The light must enter through your eyes to be effective; skin exposure has not been proven to work. Some people feel better after only one light treatment, but most people require at least a few days of treatment, and some need several weeks. Specially designed light boxes emit the proper light intensity (10,000 lux) with a minimal amount of ultraviolet light. (The lux is a measure of light intensity. By way of comparison, indoor light is about 100 lux, while a bright sunny day is 50,000 lux or more.)

You don't need a prescription to buy a light box, but it's safest to consult with your doctor before starting treatment and to report any symptoms that develop. While side effects are usually less severe than those associated with antidepressants, bright light therapy may trigger a manic episode in people who are vulnerable. Retinal damage to the eyes is rare but can occur if you take a medication or have a medical condition that increases the risk. Rashes can also occur, so discuss any skin conditions with your doctor. Other side effects include eyestrain, headaches, irritability, and difficulty sleeping (if used before bedtime).

According to estimates, light therapy doesn't provide adequate relief for 20% to 50% of people with SAD. If that's the case for you, other standard treatments for depression may help. Antidepressants may improve symptoms, and one preliminary study suggested that cognitive behavioral therapy is helpful. That study found that people who underwent cognitive behavioral therapy were less likely to have a relapse of SAD one year later compared with people who used light therapy. Individuals who used a combination of both treatments fared even better. Light therapy isn't typically covered by health insurance, but you can purchase the bright light devices in medical supply stores or online for a few hundred dollars.

Other potentially helpful treatments include daily outdoor walks, aerobic exercise, and healthy sleep habits.

Interestingly, antidepressant medications are known to promote neurogenesis in the hippocampus. This might explain why antidepressants take several weeks to start working, as it takes time for the nerves to grow and form new connections.

Antidepressant medications also boost the concentration of certain neurotransmitters, such as serotonin. These chemicals, in combination with electrical signals, allow communication within and between neurons (see Figure 2, page 10).

Family history: The role of genes

Depression tends to run in families. If you have a relative with depression, your risk of depression is much higher than that of someone without a family history of depression. A study in *JAMA Psychiatry* examined the risk of depression in 62 families across three generations. It found that young people with a depressed parent were twice as likely to develop the illness, and those with both a depressed parent and a depressed grandparent had a threefold risk of major depression.

Figure 2: How neurons communicate

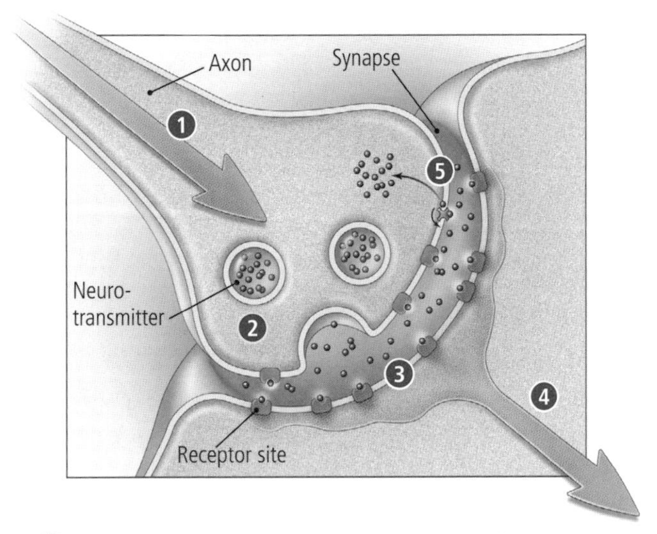

1. An electrical signal travels down the axon of a neuron.
2. The neuron releases neurotransmitter molecules.
3. The neurotransmitter molecules bind to receptor sites on another neuron.
4. The signal is picked up by the second neuron and is either passed along or halted.
5. The neuron that released the neurotransmitter takes back some of the remaining molecules, a process called reuptake.

Temperament shapes behavior

Genetics provides one perspective on how resilient you are in the face of difficult life events. But you don't need to be a geneticist to understand yourself. Another way to look at resilience is by understanding your temperament. Temperament—for example, how excitable you are or whether you tend to withdraw from or engage in social situations—is determined by your genetic inheritance and by the experiences you've had during your life. Some people are able to make better choices in life once they appreciate their habitual reactions to people and to life events.

Cognitive psychologists point out that your view of the world and, in particular, your unacknowledged assumptions about how the world works also influence how you feel. You develop your viewpoint early on and learn to automatically fall back on it when loss, disappointment, or rejection occurs. For example, you may come to see yourself as unworthy of love, so you avoid getting involved with people rather than risk losing a relationship. Or you may be so self-critical that you can't bear the slightest criticism from others, which can slow or block your career progress.

Yet while temperament or worldview may have a hand in depression, neither is unchangeable. Therapy and medications can shift thoughts and attitudes that have developed over time.

Studies of twins—including both identical twins (who share 100% of their genes) and nonidentical, or fraternal, twins (who share about half of their genes)—suggest that genes account for somewhere between one-third and two-thirds of the risk for depression.

Studying the genes involved in depression is not easy, however. Like many illnesses, depression is multigenic in origin—that is, multiple genes influence your mood and how you respond to stress. As a result, the genetic origins of mood problems are highly varied. And the way depression manifests itself is equally diverse. In fact, no two cases of depression are identical. This makes it more difficult to pinpoint the genetic causes for depression.

In 2018, a consortium of 200 international scientists published a study in *Nature Genetics* that used genetic information from 135,000 people with depression and about 345,000 mentally healthy individuals. The researchers identified 44 gene variants linked to depression, 30 of which had never been previously connected to the condition. Many of the genes play a role in how neurons grow and send signals around the brain, especially in the prefrontal cortex and a region called the anterior cingulate cortex.

The article also highlights several other interesting observations. For instance, the gene variants in question are also found in other mammals, which suggests the variants may have important roles in helping people adapt or survive. This may explain why depression persists in the human gene pool. In addition, a person's genes may affect brain development over time, including how the brain adapts to various environmental influences. The variants identified in the study are not specific to depression but are also correlated with other mental disorders, such as schizophrenia. The gene variants also overlap with genes involved in obesity and sleep quality. Finally, the authors said that the findings confirm the targets of known antidepressant medications and may offer clues for developing new drugs to treat depression.

Diagnosing depression

Although depression is by no means a silent disease, it is substantially underdiagnosed. Experts estimate that only one-third of those who have major depression get the help they need.

Primary care doctors often use short questionnaires to make an initial diagnosis. Although longer surveys are sometimes used, recent research suggests that just two questions provide a good initial means to screen for depression:

- During the past month, have you often been bothered by feeling down, depressed, or hopeless?
- During the past month, have you often been bothered by little interest or pleasure in doing things?

When other tests may be useful

Most of the time, a description of your symptoms, combined with the clinical skills of a doctor or therapist, are enough to begin treatment of depression or bipolar disorder. Sometimes, however, you need more tests to confirm a diagnosis, tease out information, or distinguish depression from other psychological or neurological problems. Your doctor may ask you to take any of the following:

- Psychological tests, during which you answer questions, respond to pictures, or perform tasks like sorting cards or drawing pictures. These tests can give your doctor a better sense of your coping mechanisms, your temperament, or your ability to organize and plan.
- Tests that look at the brain, such as an EEG or MRI, which can help identify dementia or some rare causes of depression. Both tests are painless. During an EEG, electrodes taped to your scalp pick up electrical signals. An MRI scan uses magnets, a radio wave transmitter, and a computer to pick up small changes in energy in hydrogen molecules in your brain and process the data to make a detailed picture of your brain.
- Tests for biological causes of depression, such as a blood test to check thyroid function.

A "yes" answer to even one of these questions indicates that the doctor should move on to a more thorough evaluation.

A physical exam and medical history may offer clues that point to depression caused by medication or an underlying illness. In these cases, blood tests, x-rays, or brain imaging may confirm the problem. Often, when people are unable or hesitant to recognize their own depression, their initial complaints are medical. Headaches, stomach problems, sexual difficulties, and lack of energy are among the more common medical complaints.

If your symptoms suggest depression and medical causes seem unlikely, your doctor will be interested in hearing about any feelings of sadness or hopelessness you've experienced and whether you've noticed any changes in your appetite, sex drive, or sleep patterns. He or she may also ask these questions:

- Have you or others in your family ever suffered from depression or another mental disorder? If so, how was it treated?
- Do you get satisfaction and pleasure from your life?
- Do you ever have thoughts about suicide or have you attempted suicide?
- Do you drink alcohol? If so, how often and how much?
- Do you use any drugs such as marijuana, cocaine, heroin, or prescription painkillers such as hydrocodone (Vicodin) or oxycodone (OxyContin) to get high or relax? If so, which drugs and how often?

Your health care provider might ask you to complete a checklist to explore further symptoms or subtle mood changes that otherwise might not be identified. Alternatively, the clinician may use a rating scale based on his or her observations; such scales are slightly better at detecting depression than self-reports. The doctor or therapist may also want to speak to family members who could provide a helpful perspective.

Seeking treatment

Unique differences in life experience, temperament, and biology make treatment a complex matter. No single approach works for everyone. However, many people benefit from a combination of medication and therapy. If you're overwhelmed and wondering what type of treatment to seek or what kind of therapist to approach, start with the information presented here.

Medication, therapy, or both?

No single treatment—whether it's a drug or a style of therapy—can ease depression in every case. However, research suggests you will improve your chances of getting relief if you combine drugs and therapy. One report that pooled findings from 25 studies found that adding psychotherapy to drug treatment was more helpful than medication alone in treating major depression. Earlier research suggested that one reason therapy and medication may complement each other is that they have different effects on the brain.

In addition to relieving depression, combination therapy may help ward off recurrences. A classic three-year study reported in *JAMA* tracked recurrences of major depression in about 200 people ages 60 or older. Of those who received monthly interpersonal therapy and who also took the medication nortriptyline (Aventyl, Pamelor), 80% avoided a recurrence. In contrast, the same could be said for only 57% of those who received the drug alone, 36% of those given just interpersonal therapy, and a mere 10% in the placebo group.

If your symptoms are mild or moderate, it is often reasonable to start with either medication or psychotherapy. If your depression is mild, there is a greater chance that you will respond well to psychotherapy alone. Generally, as symptoms become more severe, it is more important to consider medication earlier in your treatment.

Of course, consider all your options carefully, and discuss them with the professionals you are consulting. If one type of treatment alone isn't helping you—and especially if your depression is getting worse—you can always try combination treatment.

The three stages of treatment

Often, treatment is divided into three phases. Keep in mind, though, that there are no sharp lines dividing the phases, and very few people take a straight path through them.

1. **In the initial phase,** the aim is to relieve symptoms. Generally, this occurs within four to eight weeks, but it may take longer depending on your response to the first treatments you try.
2. **In the continuation phase,** you work with your doctor to maximize your improvements. Further treatment adjustments, such as modifying the dosage of a medication, can help. This period takes another four to five months.
3. **In the maintenance phase,** the aim is to prevent relapse. Ongoing treatment is often necessary, especially if you have already experienced several depressive episodes, have chronic low mood, or have risk factors that make a recurrence more likely.

Whom should you see for treatment?

On your road to treatment, your primary care doctor may be your first stop. A good primary care doctor can assess your symptoms with an eye to whether you have any underlying medical problems. If your doctor believes that depression is the main problem, he or she may refer you for psychotherapy or prescribe an antidepressant. Sometimes the initial response to the first treatment is good. If so, you may not need to go further.

Primary care doctors are doing more and more mental health treatment, so yours may feel comfortable trying a number of different drug treatments.

Table 1: Mental health professionals

Mental health professionals have a range of training and expertise. Of the specialists listed here, only psychiatrists and some nurses can prescribe medication. They also do psychotherapy, but it has become more common to see a non-medical professional for therapy. In many settings, various types of mental health professionals work in teams. Whatever discipline you choose, it's important to select a licensed professional. Check the relevant licensing requirements in your own state.

TITLE	DEGREE OR TRAINING	WHAT THEY DO
Psychiatrist	M.D. or D.O. (doctor of osteopathy) plus at least four years of specialized study and training in psychiatry. Medical licenses are issued by the state. The American Board of Psychiatry and Neurology certifies physicians in the specialty of psychiatry.	Provide medical and psychiatric evaluations, treat psychiatric disorders, provide psychotherapy, prescribe and monitor medications.
Psychologist	Ph.D., Psy.D., or Ed.D. in clinical, educational, counseling, or research psychology. They take a licensing exam and are licensed by individual states.	Provide psychological testing and evaluations; treat emotional and behavior problems and mental disorders, using varied techniques.
Psychiatric/mental health nurse practitioner (PMHNP)	Four-year college degree in nursing (B.S.N.) plus master of science in nursing (M.S.N.) or doctor of nursing (D.N.P.). Licensed by individual states; some states require nurses to practice under a psychiatrist's supervision.	Assess and diagnose mental health disorders, prescribe medicine, and provide therapy.
Psychiatric/mental health nurse	Associate's degree (R.N.), bachelor's degree (B.S.N.), master's degree (M.S.N. or A.P.R.N.), or doctoral degree (D.N.Sc., Ph.D.).	Varies with education level, but can include assessment of mental illnesses and psychotherapy. In certain states, nurses of this type can prescribe and monitor medication.
Social worker	Master's degree (M.A., M.S., M.S.W., or M.S.S.W.) or doctoral degree (D.S.W. or Ph.D.). In most states, they take a licensing exam to practice (for example, LCSW or LICSW).	Varies with education and training. Master's level social workers also assess and treat mental illness, including with psychotherapy.
Licensed professional counselor	Master's degree (M.A. or M.S.) in psychology, counseling, or another mental health–related field and typically two years of supervised postgraduate experience. Licensed by individual states; may also be certified by the National Board of Certified Counselors.	Assess and treat mental health conditions; provide individual, family, or group therapy.
Peer specialist	Personal experience with mental health issues. Certification varies by state; state mental health authorities can provide contact information.	Provide support and advice from the perspective of someone who has "been there."

However, if your situation is more complex, he or she is likely to refer you to a mental health professional—such as a psychiatrist, psychologist, social worker, or psychiatric nurse (see Table 1, above)—for a more detailed review.

You can also find a mental health professional through a local clinic or hospital or through recommendations from family members or friends. While some insurance plans leave the choice of therapist up to you, others limit you to professionals enrolled in their networks, so check with your insurer before choosing a provider. Finding a provider who is accepting new patients can sometimes be a challenge—particularly psychiatrists for children and adolescents, who are in short supply nationwide. Ask your primary care doctor or your health insurance company for referrals. Call several practitioners to get on their waiting lists, if necessary, and be persistent.

It may also be difficult to find a therapist who takes your health insurance, or any insurance at all, for that matter. Many psychiatrists and psychologists require you to pay for their services out of pocket, although you may be able to get partial reimbursement from your insurance company.

Since states have different requirements about who may practice as a therapist, inquire about the therapist's training, and opt only for one who has been formally trained and certified (see "10 questions to ask when choosing a therapist," page 33).

What you should know about medications

Often, medications are the first choice in treatment, especially if you're experiencing severe depression or suicidal urges. About 65% to 85% of people in that group get some relief from antidepressants, compared with 25% to 40% of people taking a placebo (a pill with no biologically active ingredient). But the very same drug that works wonders for a friend may fail to ease your symptoms. You may need to try a few different medications to find the one that works best for you with as few side effects as possible. In some cases, a doctor may prescribe a combination of antidepressants or an antidepressant along with another drug that's intended to treat anxiety or distorted thinking. A drug combination may be more effective than either drug alone.

Doctors often first prescribe medications from a class of drugs known as selective serotonin reuptake inhibitors (SSRIs). SSRIs include fluoxetine (Prozac), paroxetine (Paxil), and sertraline (Zoloft), among others. Although the side effects of each drug vary slightly from person to person, you have an equal chance of success on any of them. If you don't have a good response to the first one you try, you and your doctor may decide to switch to another.

Although in a few cases people report a change for the better as soon as one or two weeks after beginning medication, more often it takes from four to eight weeks for antidepressants to ease depression. The lag may reflect the time it takes the medications to affect processes and structures in the brain. Once you start to feel better, though, it's important to take the medication for as long as it's prescribed in order to get a full response and avoid a relapse.

If an antidepressant isn't effective, that's often because of an inadequate dose. If the medication doesn't seem to be working during the first phase of your treatment, your doctor may suggest increasing the dose. Frequently you must try different antidepressants or a combination of antidepressants with different mechanisms of action before finding what works for you. While you are using medications, the doctor prescribing them should regularly monitor both the dosages and your response. All drug treatments have advantages and disadvantages, and a doctor cannot predict how you will respond.

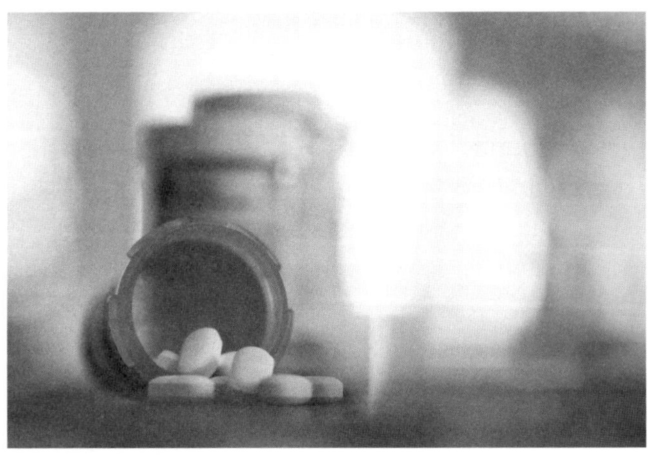

Medications are often the first choice in treatment. While there's a good chance that an antidepressant will relieve your symptoms, there's also a possibility you will encounter side effects.

While there's a good chance that an antidepressant will relieve your symptoms, there's also a possibility that you'll encounter side effects. It's frustrating but true that side effects may appear before the benefits of a drug become obvious. If you do experience side effects, the first step is to report them to your doctor. Most of them can be managed. Your doctor may be able to suggest helpful adjustments, such as changing a dose slightly or switching drugs. Many side effects diminish once your body becomes accustomed to the medication.

While many antidepressants can be safely combined, some cannot. If you switch medications, you may need a washout period (a stretch of several weeks of taking no drugs) in order to prevent dangerous interactions between a new drug and the lingering effects of the previous one.

Antidepressants are not habit-forming or addictive. However, if you are about to stop taking one of these medications, your body needs to readjust slowly, so your doctor may instruct you to reduce the dose gradually. Even so, you may experience symptoms (see "Tapering off medication," page 31).

To prevent a relapse, it's important to continue taking your medication even after you feel better. Most psychiatrists will recommend that you stay on your medication for about a year after a first episode of depression. If you have had several episodes, your doctor will probably recommend maintenance treatment indefinitely.

The problem of recurrence

When depression isn't treated, there's a high likelihood that it will recur. Roughly half of those who have a single untreated episode of major depression will go on to have another. The second untreated episode boosts the odds of a third. Once that occurs, the chances of having a fourth episode are 90%. Over a lifetime, people with untreated major depression will have an average of five to seven episodes, and episodes often accelerate, becoming more frequent and more severe.

Bipolar disorder, persistent depressive disorder, and all other mood disorders are also more likely to persist or recur if they go untreated. As with depression, episodes occur more frequently and become more intense over time. This suggests that it's best to treat major depression, bipolar disorder, and persistent depressive disorder as early as possible.

Recurrences also occur more frequently if treatment has not wholly eradicated depressive symptoms. Therefore, treatment should aim for maximum relief.

Children and teens need treatment for depression just as much as adults, especially given the pressures of social media and cyberbullying. Be aware that depressed teens may appear irritable rather than sad.

It's best to gradually increase the dose of an antidepressant (up to the recommended limits) until no further improvement is seen. Preliminary research also supports continuing with the full, therapeutic dose even after you start to feel better, rather than switching to a lower dose that may be only partially effective. Yet inadequate doses are a common problem. Primary care doctors who are less experienced with psychopharmacology (the study of the use of medications to treat mental disorders) are often reluctant to increase doses, and people who are uneasy about taking medication may be reluctant to try a higher dose.

As mentioned before, these other strategies may also help in the search for a lasting, full recovery:

- switching to a different antidepressant if the first one is not adequately effective
- combining two antidepressants that have different mechanisms of action
- adding a second drug (not primarily an antidepressant) that may augment the effect of the antidepressant you're taking
- combining medications and therapy.

Treating depression in teens and children

Childhood is supposed to be a carefree time. But some children are shaken by developmental changes and events over which they have little or no control. And depression in its many forms can affect them.

While full-blown depression most often starts in adulthood, studies show that two out of every 100 children and eight in 100 adolescents have major depression.

Persistent depressive disorder may also begin during childhood or the teenage years. Although an adult has to have depressive symptoms for at least two years before he or she is diagnosed with persistent depressive disorder, in children and teens a diagnosis is made after one year. When persistent depressive disorder appears before age 21, major depressive episodes are more likely to emerge later in life.

While rare in early childhood, bipolar disorder occasionally appears in adolescence, especially in cases where a family history of depression exists. As many as 30% of teenagers who experience an episode of major depression develop bipolar disorder in their late teens or early 20s.

Recognizing teenage depression and mania

If you are a parent of a teenager, a list of depressive symptoms may frighten you. Storminess, exhaustion, apathy, irritability, and rapid-fire changes in appetite and sleep habits are common in adolescents.

You might find yourself wondering whether a sudden loss of interest in the trumpet is a sign of depression or merely that your teen now thinks that playing in the school band is uncool. Staying up late and sleeping until noon or throwing over one interest in favor of others probably doesn't signal depression. But constant exhaustion and an unexplained withdrawal from friends and activities a child once enjoyed are reason for concern.

Because depression in children and teens often coexists with behavioral problems, anxiety, or substance abuse, experts consider a wide range of potential indicators, such as these:

- poor performance in school or frequent absences
- efforts or threats to run away from home
- bursts of unexplained irritability, shouting, or crying
- markedly increasing hostility or anger
- abuse of alcohol, drugs, or other dangerous substances
- social isolation or loss of interest in friends
- hypersensitivity to rejection or failure
- reckless behavior.

While the symptoms of depressive disorders in children, teenagers, and adults are generally similar, there are a few things worth noting. Depressed children don't act sluggish as often as depressed adults do, and depressed children and teens are more likely to appear irritable than sad. Also, young children often express feelings of depression as vague physical ailments, such as persistent stomachaches, headaches, and tiredness.

Discuss anything that concerns you with your child. If you're still concerned, speaking with your child's pediatrician or guidance counselor may help. Because depression in young children can appear so different from that of adults, a new depression diagnosis has been added to the *DSM-5* called "disruptive mood regulation disorder." This condition usually appears between the ages of 6 and 18 and is characterized by a persistently angry or irritable mood combined with regular temper outbursts.

If the child has a family history of bipolar disorder, be especially vigilant about watching for manic symptoms. The signs of manic behavior are similar in adults and children. Symptoms of mania in teens may show up as behavior that is different from the norm. They may

- talk very fast
- be very easily distracted
- get much less sleep than usual, but seem to have the same amount of energy or even more
- have extreme mood changes—for example, shifting between irritability, anger, extreme silliness, or high spirits
- indulge in, think about, or describe hypersexual behavior (relative to their norm and that of other adolescents).

If you notice these symptoms, your child's pediatrician can help you decide whether to seek professional help.

Seeking treatment for teens and children

Just like depressed adults, depressed children and teens need to get help, and the two main methods of treatment are psychotherapy and medication. But there are distinct differences between treating adults and children in most medical fields, and psychiatry is no exception.

Although many studies have shown antidepressant medications to be effective in teens and children, these drugs can also have some dangerous, unintended side effects in a small number of teens. A review by the FDA found that the average risk of suicidal thoughts in depressed teens and children who are taking an antidepressant was 4%, twice the placebo risk of 2%. Reassuringly, the number of completed suicides was not higher.

Still, the FDA responded to these concerns in 2004 by requiring that drug manufacturers place a warning about suicide risks on the package inserts that come with antidepressants. In the wake of this decision, doctors have been diagnosing depression less often and prescribing antidepressants less frequently to children and young adults.

Rather than seeing teen suicides decrease, health officials have noted a rise in the suicide rate among youths since 2004. Some experts contend that the two trends are linked (see "Can antidepressants trigger suicide?" on page 48), but other possibilities are also worth considering—for example, the negative effects of social media, cyberbullying, and access to guns. Given these unfavorable trends, it is even more important to take advantage of all effective treatments.

What does this mean for your depressed child or teen? Of course, treatment decisions should be made (with your input) with the advice of a qualified psychiatrist, preferably one who is trained to care for children. Many experts believe that appropriate use of antidepressants plays an important role in treating depression in children and teens. Like all medications, they do have some adverse effects, but they are not unusually dangerous. A clear-eyed view of benefits and risks will give a depressed child or teen the best chance of relief.

If your child does take an antidepressant, the best way to prevent a dangerous outcome is to pay close attention to how he or she is thinking and feeling. Monitor him or her for any significant negative changes in thoughts or behaviors, especially in the first few months of treatment, when the risk is thought to be the greatest.

Dealing with suicidal remarks

Children and teenagers are by nature more impulsive than adults, their emotions less tempered by experience. The connections in the brain that support impulse control do not mature until the 20s. All too often, for youngsters, suicidal thoughts translate into action. Never ignore or brush off comments about suicide or even such sweeping, dramatic statements as "I wish I were dead" or "I wish I'd never been born." Discuss them with your child.

Such sentiments may reflect nothing more than an angry outburst or hyperbole during an argument. But you can say, "Are you telling me about your frustration, or do you really feel like ending your life?" If the answers raise any concerns, if your child always refuses to engage in the conversation, or if he or she seems to exhibit signs of depression or mania, call his or her pediatrician for advice. (For more information on suicide prevention, see "Suicide: Understanding the risk," page 47.)

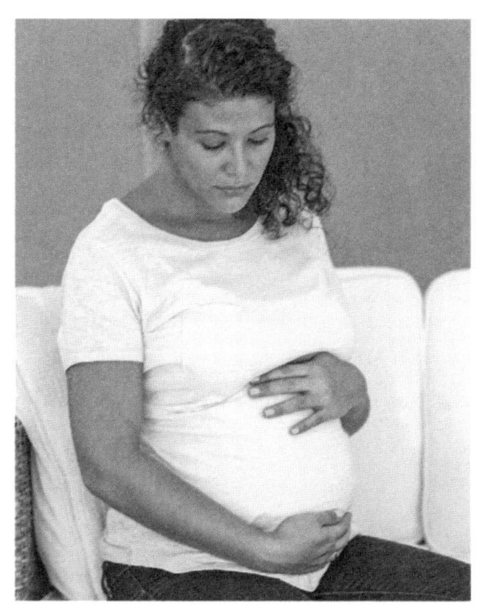

Postpartum depression is now a familiar phenomenon, but mothers-to-be often suffer depression, too. It's important for the health of both mother and child to seek treatment.

Treating depression during pregnancy

Pregnancy is often greeted with joy and happiness, but 10% to 20% of women struggle with symptoms of depression during and after pregnancy (see "Postpartum depression," page 18).

Mothers-to-be are often reluctant to seek help, but it's important to do so, for the health of both mother and child. Women who are depressed may have a hard time caring for themselves. They are more likely to miss doctors' appointments and to drink alcohol or use drugs. Their children may end up having lower birth weights and related health problems. And of course, depression can sometimes be fatal through suicide. But what type of treatment is best?

The American Psychiatric Association and a number of other health organizations recommend that women with mild depression who are pregnant, nursing, or trying to get pregnant try psychotherapy first. If you are already taking an antidepressant and wish to become pregnant, you may want to talk to your doctor about the advantages and disadvantages of gradually reducing the dose of the medication and

Postpartum depression

© monkeybusinessimages | Getty Images

More than half of women who've recently had a baby endure the weepy, anxious, emotional time known as the "baby blues." Unlike the baby blues, which usually last no more than a few weeks, postpartum depression continues and deepens.

About 10% to 15% of new mothers experience depression within three to six months after childbirth. Coming at a time that culture dictates should be happy and fulfilling, this type of depression can carry a stigma that makes some women reluctant to admit to it.

Sleep deprivation, the dramatic changes and stresses that accompany motherhood, and shifts in hormones all seem to have a hand in postpartum depression. Physical discomfort, a colicky or sick baby, financial hardship, and scant social support may also be factors.

If you suffer from postpartum depression, treatment can make a big difference for both you and your baby. Antidepressants don't pose a serious risk to nursing infants. As a safeguard, though, nursing women might opt for drugs that don't accumulate in breast milk, such as sertraline (Zoloft). Of course, other approaches, such as psychotherapy, are options as well. Your doctor can offer you advice on the best treatment for you.

Women with severe postpartum depression—particularly if it develops into psychosis—may be at risk of committing suicide or harming others, including their children. For those who do not respond to antidepressants or electroconvulsive therapy (see page 39), another option is now available. In 2019, the FDA approved the first drug specifically designed to treat postpartum depression. The drug, brexanolone (Zulresso), is a breakdown product of progesterone, the hormone that drops naturally after delivery. It must be given intravenously over several days under close supervision due to its potentially dangerous side effects, which include extreme sleepiness or loss of consciousness. As a result, it is available only through a restricted program at certified health care facilities.

shifting to therapy. Another alternative is the use of light therapy to help lift depression (see "Seasonal affective disorder: When winter brings the blues," page 9).

But for women with moderate or severe depression, for whom the burdens of the illness and the dangers to the unborn child are too great, nondrug therapy may not be enough. Of course, women should be cautious about taking any type of medication during pregnancy. These decisions are made more challenging because there is limited information about the effects of various depression medications on the unborn baby. But doctors are learning more about the risks of using—and not using—medications during pregnancy.

Weighing the risks of medication

There are three kinds of risks to a fetus when the mother is taking medication during pregnancy: risk of a congenital malformation (a problem present at birth), risk that the baby will develop symptoms shortly after birth (the neonatal period), and long-term risks.

Congenital malformations. The baby's major organs form during the first 12 weeks of the mother's pregnancy. Any medication introduced during that period could potentially increase risk of malformations. But there are ways to avoid problems.

- If you're taking antidepressants: The SSRI paroxetine (Paxil) and the non-SSRI bupropion (Wellbutrin) have been associated with heart defects in a very small number of cases. However, cause and effect have not been proved. If your mood disorder is stable on a current dose of antidepressant medication, you and your doctor may decide to continue the medication after reviewing any relevant risks. Remember that untreated depression also carries risks for the fetus.
- If you're taking mood stabilizers: Drugs such as lithium (Eskalith, Lithonate, others) or valproate (Depakote) are associated with an increase in malformations, so these should definitely be avoided early in a pregnancy. There is, however, no evidence that antipsychotic medications such as aripiprazole (Abilify, Aristada) or olanzapine (Zyprexa) increase the risk, so this category of drugs is an option for managing bipolar disorder during pregnancy.

Neonatal symptoms. When a pregnant woman takes a drug, the fetus is exposed to it. After the baby is delivered, the exposure stops, and any adverse effects of medication should go away relatively quickly. For example, if the mother has been taking anything sedating, the newborn may be more sleepy than usual, but only in the first few days of life.

With some medications, a newborn may exhibit discontinuation symptoms, such as tremor, restlessness, and increased crying. Paroxetine has been most often associated with this problem, because it leaves the baby's system more quickly than other antidepressants. That rapid decline exaggerates the effect. Fortunately, these symptoms trail off within days without any need for special treatment.

Long-term risks. Many parents are worried that psychiatric drugs will cause long-term harm to their children. These kinds of risks are very hard to study, so there are limited data available. So far, however, there is no evidence that exposure to antidepressants via amniotic fluid or breast milk causes any long-term harm to a child's intellectual, emotional, or behavioral development.

Putting it all together

The best time for decision making about the use of medication during pregnancy is before getting pregnant, since the first trimester is the stage when the baby's major organs are forming. Neonatal symptoms are a concern, but are fortunately transient. We have limited information about long-term risks.

Remember that mood disorders, if they go untreated, also present risk. A woman who is depressed may get poorer care and is more likely to use substances that are well known to be harmful to the unborn baby, especially alcohol and tobacco. Depressed women have more pregnancy complications than nondepressed women and are more likely to give birth to an infant who develops more slowly than average.

Therefore, each pregnant woman with depression needs to weigh the risks of untreated depression against the short- and long-term risks of taking medication. There is evidence for avoiding paroxetine, lithium, and valproate, but there are many other good medication options for women who are trying to manage a moderate to severe mood problem.

Treating depression in the elderly

Depression is not a normal part of aging, although many older people and their caregivers think the two go hand in hand. As people age, they do often encounter many familiar sources of depression, including health problems and the loss of loved ones. But these problems do not necessarily lead to depression, though it may not always be clear to people how to distinguish one from the other (see "How grief differs from depression," below). Depression can also be difficult to distinguish from dementia (see "Is it dementia or depression?" on page 20).

When depression does arise, it should be treated, no matter how old a person is. One long-term study found that older adults who suffered from chronic depression lasting at least six years had an 88% higher risk of developing cancer. Other studies suggest that older adults who are depressed are at greater risk of developing Alzheimer's or experiencing a decline in mental powers and are more likely to have diminished

How grief differs from depression

While grief is a natural response to the loss of a loved one, the grieving process is unique for each person. Two common expressions of bereavement—feeling intensely sad and shying away from normal routines and activities—are also common in depression. And in some people, the death of a loved one can actually precipitate major depression. So how can you tell the difference—and when should you seek treatment?

During grief, painful feelings come in waves and are often intertwined with happy memories of the person who died. During depression, mood and thoughts tend to be negative most of the time. Feelings of worthlessness and self-loathing are also common in depression, whereas people who are grieving maintain their self-esteem.

Consult a professional if dense, negative, low mood is combined with worthlessness, self-loathing, and low self-esteem. Or seek help if discomfort is persistent, approaches being unbearable, or is severely interfering with functioning.

Is it dementia or depression?

In older adults who experience intellectual decline, it's sometimes difficult to tell whether the cause is dementia or depression. Both disorders are common in later years, and each can lead to the other.

Depression in the elderly can also lead to a phenomenon called pseudodementia—an apparent intellectual decline that stems from a lack of energy or effort. People with this problem are often forgetful, move slowly, and have low motivation as well as mental slowing. They may or may not appear depressed. This syndrome responds well to treatments for depression. As mood improves, a person's energy, ability to concentrate, and intellectual functioning usually return to previous levels.

Although depression and dementia share certain traits, there are some differences that help distinguish one from the other:

- Decline in mental functioning tends to be more rapid with depression than with Alzheimer's or another type of dementia.
- Unlike people with Alzheimer's, people with depression are usually not disoriented.
- People with depression have difficulty concentrating, whereas those affected by Alzheimer's have problems with short-term memory.
- Writing, speaking, and motor skills aren't usually impaired in depression.
- Depressed people are more likely to notice and comment on their memory problems, while those with Alzheimer's may seem indifferent to such changes.

Since there is no simple test that can reveal whether someone has depression or dementia, treatment is often worth trying. If depression is at the root, treatment can produce dramatic improvement.

immune responses, which may affect their ability to fight off infections or other kinds of disease.

Independent of the other medical problems associated with depression, treatment of depression can dramatically improve a person's quality of life.

Depression is not a normal part of aging and should be treated. Studies show that older adults with depression are at higher risk for dementia and are more likely to have diminished immune responses.

Although many people face obstacles to treatment for depression, an older adult's road to recovery can seem especially difficult. For example, in older people, depression may occur in conjunction with other illnesses that mask the depressive symptoms. Health care professionals may treat the medical illness and overlook the depression.

In addition, depending on culture and point of view, some seniors may feel there is a stigma attached to mental health treatment. Older adults are sometimes more sensitive to side effects of antidepressants. These drugs also may not mix well with medication they take for other illnesses. For these reasons, as many as 40% of older people taking antidepressants quit or repeatedly miss doses because of side effects, memory problems, or difficulty keeping track of complicated drug regimens.

Although seniors with severe depression tend to respond to antidepressant drugs about as well as younger people, they sometimes improve more slowly and relapse sooner. However, a knowledgeable doctor can help with these concerns.

Finding the right medication

There are many drugs that can be used to treat mood problems. But finding the right one can be a lengthy process, and the choice can be more complicated than you might imagine. Just because a particular drug worked for a friend doesn't mean it will work for you. Also, be skeptical about advertisements for genetic testing kits that supposedly help determine which depression treatment would work best for you. At least for now, there's no evidence that any of these tests deliver on that promise (see "Genetic testing to guide depression treatment: Don't waste your money," below).

If the first drug you try doesn't yield a positive effect after four to eight weeks of treatment, your doctor may increase your dose. If that doesn't work, he or she may suggest that you switch to another drug in the same class or a drug in a different class. You can try several different antidepressants in sequence until you find one that helps you. Your doctor may also recommend adding psychotherapy if that hasn't been part of your treatment plan. The combination of medication and therapy often works best.

Having to go through all of these steps may sound discouraging, but finding the treatment that works for you will be worth the effort. One major study, the Sequenced Treatment Alternatives to Relieve Depression (STAR*D) trial, took a close look at how people respond to "real world" treatment, where they try a series of treatments until they find one that helps. More than half of the people who participated in the study went into remission after trying two treatments. Over all, 70% of all the people who didn't withdraw from the study eventually got relief from all their symptoms of depression.

This chapter will help you understand the different classes of medications, their pluses and minuses, and why a doctor might opt for a less common drug over the ones you've heard about most often.

Genetic testing to guide depression treatment: Don't waste your money

For many people, finding the best drug to treat their depression is a frustrating process of trial and error. Several genetic testing companies promise to streamline the process. You just swab your inner cheek to provide a DNA sample and shell out a few hundred dollars (typical out-of-pocket costs run between about $250 and $400). The companies then search for a handful of genes that may affect how you metabolize or respond to different antidepressant drugs.

But while those genes may influence the levels of medications in your bloodstream, that's not enough to predict your response to those drugs. Many other factors—including age, diet, hormone levels, gut bacteria, and other medications you may be taking—are far more important in determining how you metabolize a specific antidepressant and how your brain and body react to that drug.

At least 10 studies have reported outcomes from people with depression who used commercially available gene test panels to guide antidepressant choice, according to a brief report in *JAMA Psychiatry* in 2018. Most studies were completely unblinded—that is, both doctors and patients knew a special test was given to help with drug selection. Even with that bias, the use of gene results showed no evidence of effectiveness. A few studies were partially blinded, but doctors and patients still knew some patients got a special test. In these studies, too, the tests failed to show value on their key measures of efficacy.

Not only has an American Psychiatric Association task force recommended against the use of these tests, the FDA has denounced them as well. In a safety communication, the agency said results from genetic testing for depression treatment could even lead to inappropriate treatment choices that might harm people. The FDA also has also warned companies selling the tests that they cannot legally make specific recommendations based on the test results.

How your doctor makes a choice

Psychiatrists and doctors who prescribe antidepressants choose a particular drug and dosage based on many factors, including the following:

Diagnosis. Certain drugs are a better choice for specific symptoms and types of depression. For example, an antidepressant that makes you sleepy may be better when insomnia is an issue. The severity of your illness or the presence of anxiety, obsessions, or compulsions may also dictate the choice of one drug over another.

Side effects. You may first want to choose a drug based on which side effect you most want to avoid. Medications vary in the likelihood they will cause such problems as sexual effects, weight gain, or sedation. You can find information on medication side effects in the following sections and in Table 2, page 23.

Age. As you age, your body tends to break drugs down more slowly. Thus, older people may need a lower dose. For children, only a few medications have been studied carefully.

Health. If you have certain health problems, it's best to avoid certain drugs. For example, your doctor will want to consider factors such as heart disease or neurological illnesses when recommending a drug. For this reason, it's important to discuss medical problems with a primary care doctor or psychiatrist before starting an antidepressant.

Medications, supplements, and diet. When combined with certain drugs or substances, antidepressants may not work as well, or they may have worrisome or dangerous side effects. For example, combining an SSRI or another antidepressant with the herbal remedy St. John's wort can boost serotonin to dangerous (and in rare cases fatal) levels. Mixing St. John's wort with other drugs—including certain drugs to control HIV infection, cancer medications, and birth control pills—might lower their effectiveness. Women receiving tamoxifen for breast cancer should take an antidepressant that does not interfere with tamoxifen's effectiveness. Eating certain foods, such as aged cheeses and cured meats, while taking a class of antidepressants called monoamine oxidase inhibitors (MAOIs) can cause a dangerous rise in blood pressure.

Alcohol or drugs. Alcohol and other substances can cause depression and make antidepressants less effective. Doctors often treat alcohol or drug addiction first if they believe either is causing the depression. In many instances, simultaneous treatment for addiction and depression is warranted.

Personal and family mental health and medication history. If you or a member of your family has had a good response to a medication in the past, that information may guide your choice. Depending on the nature and course of your depression (for example, if your depression is long-lasting or difficult to treat), you may need a higher dose or a combination of drugs. This may also be true if an antidepressant has stopped working for you, which may occur after you've used it for some time or after you've stopped and restarted treatment with it.

Cost. Many older antidepressants are available in generic form. Since they're likely to be as effective as newer drugs, you won't lose anything by trying a less costly generic version first.

Your preference. Once you have learned as much as you can about the treatment options, your doctor will want to know what approach makes most sense given your lifestyle, your interests, and your judgment.

Medications for depression and persistent depressive disorder

Antidepressants are big business for pharmaceutical companies, which have promoted them with intense marketing campaigns. Today, the most commonly prescribed antidepressants are the SSRIs, which doctors often turn to first since they are often most familiar with them. However, since the early 1990s, additional antidepressants have joined the SSRIs as good first-line treatments. These include the serotonin-norepinephrine reuptake inhibitors (SNRIs), as well as the atypical antidepressants mirtazapine and bupropion. Many of these drugs are now available in generic versions. The first generation of antidepressants—tricyclic antidepressants (TCAs) and monoamine oxidase inhibitors (MAOIs)—are now rarely used for first-line treatment.

Continued on page 25

Table 2: Medications used for depression, persistent depressive disorder, and bipolar disorder

GENERIC NAME (BRAND NAME)	SIDE EFFECTS
Selective serotonin reuptake inhibitors (SSRIs)*	
citalopram (Celexa) escitalopram (Lexapro) fluoxetine (Prozac) fluvoxamine (Luvox) paroxetine (Paxil) paroxetine mesylate (Pexeva) sertraline (Zoloft)	Nausea; diarrhea or constipation; weight loss or gain; anxiety; insomnia (occasionally drowsiness); headache; sweating; dry mouth; sexual problems (see "Sexuality and SSRIs," page 26). Bleeding problems are uncommon, but do sometimes occur.
Serotonin modulators*	
nefazodone (Serzone)	Liver injury (requires close monitoring); nausea; drowsiness; dry mouth; dizziness; constipation.
trazodone (Desyrel)	Sedation (used more often as a sleep aid because of this effect); dizziness; dry mouth; nausea; drops in blood pressure; headache. Rarely: persistent painful erection (priapism); disturbance of heart rhythm (arrhythmia).
vilazodone (Viibryd)	Diarrhea; nausea; sexual dysfunction; dizziness; sleep problems; vomiting.
vortioxetine (Trintellix, formerly called Brintellix)	Nausea; less commonly vomiting and constipation; may have less sexual dysfunction than SSRIs.
Serotonin-norepinephrine reuptake inhibitors (SNRIs)*	
desvenlafaxine (Pristiq)	Loss of appetite; dry mouth; dizziness; sleep problems; drowsiness; diarrhea or constipation; mild headache; nausea. High blood pressure may occur, but is uncommon.
duloxetine (Cymbalta)	Nausea; dry mouth; dizziness; sexual problems; anxiety; loss of appetite; at higher doses, rise in blood pressure.
levomilnacipran (Fetzima)	Nausea; constipation; excessive sweating; increased heart rate; sexual problems; vomiting.
venlafaxine (Effexor)	Nausea; insomnia; dry mouth; dizziness; sleep problems; sexual problems; blurred vision; anxiety; loss of appetite; at higher doses, rise in blood pressure.
Atypical antidepressants*	
bupropion (Wellbutrin)	Anxiety; dry mouth; sweating; loss of appetite; sleep problems. Can trigger seizures and psychosis in people who have an underlying condition that makes them vulnerable to these problems.
mirtazapine (Remeron)	Drowsiness or sedation; constipation; dry mouth; increased appetite; weight gain.
Tricyclic antidepressants (TCAs)*	
amitriptyline (generic) clomipramine (Anafranil) imipramine (Tofranil) nortriptyline (Aventyl, Pamelor) protriptyline (Vivactil)	Dry mouth; blurred vision; dizziness when changing postures (for example, going from sitting to standing); drowsiness; weight gain; constipation; trouble urinating; disturbance of heart rhythm (arrhythmia).
Monoamine oxidase inhibitors (MAOIs)*	
isocarboxazid (Marplan) phenelzine (Nardil) selegiline transdermal (Emsam)** tranylcypromine (Parnate)	Dizziness when changing postures; diarrhea; nervousness or trembling; drowsiness; mild headache; weight gain, with cravings for sweets; disturbed sleep. Rarely: dangerously high blood pressure if foods containing tyramine are eaten; abnormal liver function.

All antidepressants may cause agitation and restlessness; involuntary movements, such as tics and tremors; and suicidal thoughts or behaviors, particularly in the first weeks of treatment. These side effects are rare.

***An additional side effect for this drug may include mild redness or irritation where the patch is placed.*

Table 2 *continued*

GENERIC NAME (BRAND NAME)	SIDE EFFECTS
Lithium	
lithium carbonate (Eskalith, Lithane, Lithobid, Lithonate)	Excessive thirst; frequent urination; memory problems and poor concentration; tremors; weight gain; drowsiness; diarrhea; occasional problems with low thyroid function; more rarely, heart or kidney problems over time.
Anticonvulsants	
carbamazepine (Tegretol)	Fatigue; nausea; dizziness; unsteadiness; double or blurred vision. Rarely: lowered blood cell counts; impaired liver function.
gabapentin (Neurontin)	Coordination problems; abnormal dreams or thinking; anemia; irregular heartbeat; agitation or nervousness.
lamotrigine (Lamictal)	Fatigue; rash; headache; blurred or double vision; dizziness; nausea; memory or concentration problems. Rarely: lowered blood cell counts; impaired liver function.
topiramate (Topamax)	Lack of coordination; dizziness; abdominal pain; fatigue; memory difficulties; nervousness; drowsiness; speech problems; nausea; tremors; sensations such as tingling, burning, or hypersensitivity; rapid movement of the eyes; upper respiratory infections; mood problems. Rarely: abdominal pain; weight loss.
valproate (Depakote)	Nausea, indigestion, vomiting, or diarrhea; tremors; sedation; hair loss; increased appetite and weight gain. Rarely: impaired liver function; lowered blood cell counts; inflamed pancreas. May raise the risk of polycystic ovary syndrome.
Antipsychotics	
aripiprazole (Abilify, Aristada)	Nausea; vomiting; increased appetite and weight gain; constipation or diarrhea; heartburn; headache; dizziness; restlessness; anxiety; insomnia; stomach pain; increased risk of stroke; high fever; rigid muscles; shaking; confusion; abnormal movements of the face, tongue, or other body parts; uncontrollable urges to gamble, binge eat, shop, and have sex.
brexpiprazole (Rexulti)	Weight gain, dizziness, drowsiness; agitation or restlessness; high doses or long-term use may cause abnormal movements of the face, tongue, or other body parts.
clozapine (Clozaril)	Drowsiness; excess salivation; dry mouth; blurred vision; constipation; dizziness; transient fever; rapid heartbeat; seizures at higher doses; potentially dangerous drop in white blood cell counts, which requires frequent, regular monitoring.
lurasidone (Latuda)	Restlessness or a need to move; difficulty moving; slow movement; muscle stiffness; tremor; nausea.
olanzapine (Zyprexa)	Drowsiness; weight gain; dry mouth; dizziness; weakness; upset stomach or constipation; anxiety or agitation; headache; fast heartbeat. Rarely: movement disorders; seizures; very low blood pressure.
quetiapine (Seroquel)	Headache; drowsiness; dizziness; constipation; dry mouth; weight gain; rapid heart rate or low blood pressure; upset stomach; altered liver or thyroid function. Rarely: movement disorders; low blood cell counts; seizures.
risperidone (Risperdal)	Drowsiness; anxiety; dizziness; constipation or diarrhea; nausea or stomach upset; rapid heart rate; increased dreaming; visual disturbances; weight gain. Rarely: movement disorders.
Anti-anxiety medications	
benzodiazepines, including alprazolam (Xanax), clonazepam (Klonopin), lorazepam (Ativan)	Clumsiness or unsteadiness; drowsiness; cognitive impairment; dizziness; headache; tolerance to the drug, requiring increasing doses.
buspirone (BuSpar)	Chest pain; dizziness; headache; nausea.
Note: For precautions regarding the use of any of these medications during pregnancy, see "Treating depression during pregnancy," page 17.	

Continued from page 22

Studies in the past several decades have shown that all antidepressants are about equally effective. Since, as mentioned previously, people respond differently to different antidepressants, the variety of available medications increases the chances of finding a drug (or a combination) that works for you. Moreover, if a certain side effect is bothering you, you may be able to avoid it by switching drugs, since the various medications often have different side-effect profiles.

Selective serotonin reuptake inhibitors (SSRIs)

SSRIs stepped into the spotlight in the late 1980s. The serotonin system involves many regions of the brain and affects mood, arousal, anxiety, impulses, and aggression. SSRIs slow the reuptake of serotonin—that is, they slow reabsorption by the neurons that released it. (For an illustration of reuptake, see Figure 2, page 10.) By blocking reuptake, the drugs permit serotonin to work for a longer time at receptor sites. SSRIs also appear to change the number and sensitivity of receptors and to indirectly influence other neurotransmitters, including norepinephrine and dopamine.

Fluoxetine, the first SSRI (introduced in 1988), quickly became a celebrity, marketed under the name Prozac. Not only did it relieve depressive symptoms in many people, but—in some individuals—it also appeared to help with a wide variety of problems, including anxiety, shyness (social phobia), obsessions (obsessive-compulsive disorder), and eating disorders (anorexia or bulimia). Other similarly effective SSRIs have since been introduced to the market.

SSRIs have several advantages over the TCAs and MAOIs that came before them. Unlike TCAs, they rarely cause dry mouth, constipation, or dizziness. Nor are they likely to disrupt heart rhythms, a potentially fatal effect of an overdose of TCAs. And with SSRIs, you don't have to worry about dietary restrictions, as you would if you took MAOIs.

On the other hand, SSRI side effects can be uncomfortable. The best known of these are sexual side effects. It's fairly common for men taking these medications to have problems sustaining an erection. Both sexes may find that the drugs dampen desire or make it difficult to reach orgasm (see "Sexuality and SSRIs," page 26).

Other side effects include nausea, insomnia, headaches, and a slight increased risk of excessive bleeding, particularly if taken with aspirin, nonsteroidal anti-inflammatory drugs (NSAIDs) or the blood thinner warfarin (Coumadin).

Still under debate is the extent to which SSRIs may increase suicide risk. Suicidal thinking (but not actual suicide) has been seen to increase in a small percentage of children and young adults taking these drugs (see "Can antidepressants trigger suicide?" on page 48 and "Treating depression in teens and children," page 15).

Sometimes an SSRI will stop working for you—a phenomenon doctors call "Prozac poop-out." Clinicians observe this experience, but there is no good explanation for why it happens. Common solutions are to increase your dose or to add or switch to another drug.

Another potential problem is that SSRIs can interact with certain antihistamines, anticonvulsants, other antidepressants, mood stabilizers, and herbal supplements. For example, one such problem, called serotonin syndrome, can occur if you take St. John's wort along with SSRIs. This condition is marked by a racing heart, fever, sweating, high blood pressure, trembling, and confusion. Potentially, at least, it can also occur when an SSRI is combined with lithium.

Although these side effects may seem daunting, keep in mind that many people tolerate these medications without difficulty. The main advantage of SSRIs and other newer antidepressants isn't necessarily that they cause fewer side effects or less discomfort. It's that the most dangerous side effects tend to occur less frequently.

Serotonin-norepinephrine reuptake inhibitors (SNRIs)

As their name suggests, the serotonin-norepinephrine reuptake inhibitors (SNRIs)—venlafaxine (Effexor), desvenlafaxine (Pristiq), and duloxetine (Cymbalta)—slow the reuptake of both serotonin and norepinephrine. Consequently, they are sometimes called "dual-action" drugs. In addition to depression, these medications have been used to treat anxiety and chronic pain.

Nausea is the most common side effect of this class of drugs. Taking doses with food may help. Nausea tends to improve over time. Other side effects are dizziness, sweating, headaches, and sexual dysfunction. Venlafaxine and desvenlafaxine can cause high blood pressure at higher doses.

Atypical antidepressants

These medications are called "atypical" because each one has a unique mechanism of action. In effect, each is the only member of the category.

Bupropion (Wellbutrin) has been available since the late 1980s, about as long as fluoxetine (Prozac). It works on the neurotransmitters dopamine and norepinephrine. (It has little effect on serotonin or other neurotransmitters.) It is thus a good medication to try for people who have not gotten relief from an SSRI. Another advantage is that it does not cause sexual problems and it may help people who have sexual difficulties caused by another antidepressant. Bupropion can cause seizures at high doses and should be avoided in people with seizure disorders. Other side effects include dry mouth, nausea, trouble sleeping, dizziness, and anxiety.

Mirtazapine (Remeron) is not a reuptake blocker, but it does increase the release of norepi-

Sexuality and SSRIs

One drawback to SSRIs is that they frequently dampen sexual response. (In this regard, they aren't alone. With some exceptions, such as bupropion [Wellbutrin] and mirtazapine [Remeron], other antidepressants also cause the problem to almost the same degree and frequency.) In addition to reducing interest in sex, SSRIs can make it difficult to become aroused, sustain arousal, and reach orgasm. Some people taking SSRIs aren't able to have an orgasm at all. These symptoms tend to become more common with age.

If you experience any sexual problems while taking an SSRI, talk with your doctor or therapist. About 35% to 50% of people with untreated major depression experience some type of sexual dysfunction prior to treatment, so in some cases, sexual difficulties stem not from the medication, but rather from the underlying depression.

If medication is the problem, sexual side effects sometimes subside with time, so it's worth waiting a while to see if problems diminish. This is a particularly good strategy if the medication is easing your depression significantly. If side effects persist, your doctor or therapist may suggest one of the following strategies:

Lowering the dose. Sexual side effects may subside at a lower, though still therapeutic, dose.

Scheduling sex. Your medication may produce more pronounced side effects at particular times of the day, for example, within a few hours of taking it. If so, you can try scheduling sexual activity for the time when side effects are least bothersome—or take the drug at a different time.

Taking a drug holiday. Depending on how long the drug usually remains in your body, you might stop taking it for a few days—for example, before a weekend, if that's when you hope to have sex. This isn't spontaneous, but it can work if you carefully follow your doctor's directions about how to stop and resume your medication. However, there is always a chance that this might cause a relapse, especially if it is one of the drugs that leaves your system relatively rapidly.

Switching to a different drug. Certain antidepressants, such as bupropion, mirtazapine, TCAs, and MAOIs, are less likely to cause sexual problems. Bupropion, which affects both norepinephrine and dopamine, can sometimes improve sexual response.

Adding a drug. For some men, taking sildenafil (Viagra) or tadalafil (Cialis) can alleviate SSRI-induced erectile dysfunction. For women, these drugs haven't proven very helpful. However, men and women may both benefit from adding bupropion to their treatment. This medication has been found to counter SSRI-induced sexual dysfunction, boost sexual drive and arousal, and increase the intensity or duration of an orgasm. Another drug, buspirone (BuSpar), can restore the ability to have an orgasm and increase libido.

Meeting with a therapist. Even when physical issues or medication are at the root of sexual problems, psychological issues often become interwoven. For example, a few episodes of erectile dysfunction may cause a man to withdraw from sex and his partner to feel rejected. These issues can lead the couple to retreat further from intimacy. Working with a sex therapist or general therapist can help couples explore their sexual concerns, learn to better communicate their needs, and expand their repertoire of sexual activities.

nephrine and serotonin. It can be quite sedating, so is a good choice for people who are having trouble sleeping. It also does not appear to cause sexual problems. The most problematic side effect is an increase in appetite and weight.

Serotonin modulators

Serotonin modulators (as compared to SSRIs) affect serotonin more broadly. The drugs in this class tend to work in several ways simultaneously—blocking reuptake of serotonin, but also stimulating its release and influencing the functioning of a variety of receptors.

Nefazodone (Serzone) is a weak inhibitor of the reuptake of serotonin and norepinephrine. Its most serious side effect is liver damage, causing it to be used rarely in the United States. Other side effects include nausea, sleepiness, dry mouth, dizziness, and constipation. It causes less sexual dysfunction than SSRIs.

Trazodone (Desyrel, generic) is currently used more often as a sleep aid for people with depression than it is for treatment of depression itself. It works through a variety of serotonin receptors, while also affecting receptors for other chemical messengers. Side effects include sedation (which is sometimes desirable), dizziness, dry mouth, and nausea. Some people also experience blood pressure fluctuations and headaches.

Vilazodone (Viibryd) works by inhibiting reuptake of serotonin and stimulating serotonin receptors. Side effects include diarrhea, nausea (and sometimes vomiting), sexual dysfunction, dizziness, and sleep problems.

Vortioxetine (Trintellix) inhibits the reuptake of serotonin, but also affects a variety of serotonin receptors. It appears to affect concentrations of several chemical messengers in the brain. The most common side effect is nausea, which sometimes gets better with time. There is evidence that this medication is tolerated well over all (that is, relatively few patients stop taking it because of side effects). There is a low incidence of vomiting and constipation. This medication may cause less sexual dysfunction than other antidepressants.

Tricyclic antidepressants (TCAs)

TCAs, named for their three-ring molecular structure, have been used since the 1960s. Before the introduction of SSRIs, they were the most frequently prescribed antidepressants. These drugs, like the SNRIs, increase the availability of both norepinephrine and serotonin by slowing their reabsorption into the neurons that released them. At the same time, though, TCAs influence another neurotransmitter, acetylcholine, which can lead to dry mouth, dizziness, constipation, blurred vision when reading, and trouble urinating. These drugs can also cause weight gain. Commonly prescribed TCAs include nortriptyline (Aventyl, Pamelor) and imipramine (Tofranil).

Their biggest disadvantage is a dangerously abnormal heart rhythm that can occur if a person overdoses on the drug—for example, during a suicide attempt. Given the drugs' effects on heart rhythm, they also are usually not prescribed for people with heart disease.

These drawbacks make TCAs less appealing as a first-line treatment. Nonetheless, they can be prescribed safely in many cases and may be an excellent option for people who have tried many other antidepressants without getting relief.

Monoamine oxidase inhibitors (MAOIs)

The neurotransmitters norepinephrine and serotonin are members of a class of compounds called monoamines. They are normally broken down in the body by the enzyme monoamine oxidase (MAO). Monoamine oxidase inhibitors (MAOIs) block this enzyme, thereby raising the concentration of norepinephrine and serotonin in the space between neurons, where they can bind to nerve cell receptors.

MAOIs may be especially helpful for people with a form of depression that is sometimes called atypical depression, meaning that it is accompanied by unusual symptoms, such as weight gain and excessive sleep, in contrast to the more typical symptoms of weight loss and sleeplessness. These drugs can also be used to treat the extreme anxiety of panic attacks.

The two most commonly used MAOIs are phenelzine (Nardil) and tranylcypromine (Parnate). As with other antidepressants, all MAOIs have a variety of side effects. They can cause sedation, insomnia, and weight gain. MAOIs can also leave you feeling stimulated or restless. Dizziness sometimes occurs, which is particularly troublesome to older adults who are more prone to disabling falls. In addition, a relatively small number of people taking MAOIs develop liver damage.

But the greatest source of inconvenience is that people taking MAOIs must restrict their intake of tyramine, an amino acid that also happens to be a monoamine. Tyramine is usually broken down by the MAO enzyme. When the drug disables the enzyme, tyramine concentrations can rise to unsafe levels, potentially causing a rapid increase in blood pressure that can—rarely—lead to a stroke. Tyramine is found in foods such as aged cheese, broad bean pods, cured meats, and tap beer. There are moderate amounts in wine and in canned or bottled beer.

The American Psychiatric Association's current guidelines on treating depression recommend that MAOIs be used only by people who don't respond to other treatments.

Adding mood stabilizers or other drugs

People with depression may also experience mood swings—like the ups and downs seen in various forms of bipolar disorder—so a mood stabilizer, such as lithium or valproate (Depakote), may be added to treatment. Even if you don't have cycling moods, these medications can sometimes build on the effects of an antidepressant, improving your response. For example, the antipsychotic medication aripiprazole

Ketamine: A new, fast-acting drug for stubborn depression?

In the 1970s, ketamine was used in the Vietnam War as a battlefield anesthetic. In the 1990s, thanks to its hallucinogenic properties, it became popular as an illegal club drug called "Special K." Today, a reformulated, low-dose version of ketamine is available by prescription for people with hard-to-treat depression. However, it is still considered a novel treatment in its infancy.

The mood-related benefits may stem from the fact that ketamine works through a unique (yet not fully understood) mechanism. The drug modulates the activity of glutamate, a brain chemical thought to play a role in stimulating the growth of new brain connections. It also appears to encourage the release of other molecules that help neurons communicate with each other along new pathways. Known as synaptogenesis, this process likely affects mood and thought patterns.

Most of the research on ketamine's potential benefits for depression and other mood disorders was done using an intravenous (IV) version of the drug. Studies show that a single infusion of ketamine can improve mood within two to four hours in some people with treatment-resistant depression (depression that hasn't responded to at least two different antidepressants). Some people who are so deeply depressed that they are contemplating suicide have been helped by ketamine.

Starting around 2014, specialized clinics throughout the United States began offering IV ketamine infusions "off-label," as the drug was approved as an anesthetic but not specifically to treat depression. But in 2019, the FDA approved a nasal spray version of the drug called esketamine (Spravato). Because the side effects of the drug include sedation and dissociation (an unsettling feeling of being disconnected from one's thoughts, feelings, memories, or surroundings), people need to be closely monitored for two hours after taking the drug. As such, esketamine can be administered only in a certified medical office. Other possible side effects include nausea, dizziness, anxiety, and increased blood pressure.

While the effects from the IV treatment may last for a few weeks to a month, effects from the nasal spray last for a day or a few days. In both instances the dose is much lower than would be used for anesthesia or when used recreationally.

However, ketamine doesn't work for everyone. The benefits vary depending on how long a person has been depressed, how severe the symptoms are, and how many other drugs he or she has tried without seeing improvement. For people with less severe depression, ketamine may be effective in as many as 60% of those who try it. Among those with more persistent, severe depression, only about 30% to 40% may experience relief.

People who improve after one to three ketamine treatments are most likely to find that future treatments maintain that level of improvement rather than delivering further relief. But as of 2020, there are no standard treatment guidelines for ketamine therapy. Many studies included eight initial treatments. After that, doctors can help patients decide whether to taper off or stop ketamine or continue treatments at longer intervals.

(Abilify, Aristada) is sometimes taken in conjunction with an antidepressant to boost the effect of the antidepressant. Medications in a variety of classes can be used for this purpose.

Medications for bipolar disorder

Stabilizing mood is the chief goal of treatment for bipolar disorder. By preventing manic and depressive episodes, these medications rein in the highs and lows of this illness.

Lithium (Eskalith, Lithonate, others) is the most widely known medication used to treat bipolar disorder. In clinical use for at least half a century, it is still the most effective of all the mood stabilizers for treating and preventing bipolar disorder. Some people have trouble tolerating the side effects, however, or are troubled by the need for periodic blood tests to check that the medication is at a therapeutic level.

The alternatives to lithium are antipsychotic and anticonvulsant medications. There are several medications in each category (see Table 2, page 23), many of which are used in combination. Depending on the nature of your illness, your doctor may prescribe any of these along with an antidepressant or anti-anxiety medication.

You may need to continue medications indefinitely to keep your mood stable. The likelihood of having a relapse when you stop treatment is great, especially if you've had two or more episodes of mania or depression.

Experts now believe that the more episodes of depression or mania you've experienced, the more intense and frequent your subsequent episodes may be. Therefore, for people with bipolar disorder, maintenance therapy is often the best strategy.

Lithium

Lithium is one of the oldest drugs used in psychiatry. Since the 1960s, it has proved very effective in preventing the mood swings of bipolar illness.

Common side effects of lithium include thirst, nausea, and tremors. While lithium can alter laboratory measures of kidney, heart, or thyroid function, studies of people who have taken lithium for many years are reassuring. Significant damage to the kidneys is quite rare, and changes to the heart noted on electrocardiograms are almost always harmless. Long-term lithium use can cause thyroid problems in up to half the people who use it, but these problems are easily treated.

There is a narrow dose range in which lithium is effective. Since doses that are too high can rapidly become toxic, doctors use periodic blood tests to monitor lithium levels. Dehydration and diuretics (which are taken for high blood pressure) can increase the concentration of lithium in the blood, making the risk of toxicity greater. Early symptoms of toxicity include diarrhea, vomiting, drowsiness, weakness, and loss of coordination. Without treatment, toxicity can lead to confusion, agitation, unstable blood pressure, stupor, or coma. But these problems are quite rare if you know the risk and your doctor monitors your blood levels regularly.

Because lithium takes days or weeks to become effective in someone who is going through a manic phase, doctors often prescribe additional medications to help in the meantime.

While lithium has some drawbacks, a survey conducted by two large health plans indicates that it's better at preventing suicide than another frequently prescribed bipolar disorder treatment, valproate (see "Anticonvulsants," page 30). Valproate is at least as effective as lithium for mania, but lithium provides better protection against depression, the state in which people with bipolar disorder are most likely to commit suicide. Other research shows that when people stop taking lithium, the suicide rate rises for several months, although tapering off the drug gradually can reduce the risk.

Antipsychotics

Antipsychotic medications have become important treatments for the depression that occurs in bipolar disorder. An antipsychotic can also be helpful if distorted or psychotic thinking occurs as part of an episode of mania.

There is good evidence for trying quetiapine (Seroquel) or lurasidone (Latuda) first. Aripiprazole (Abilify, Aristada), olanzapine (Zyprexa), and risperidone (Risperdal) are other antipsychotics that may be offered. In general, many antipsychotics have similar side effects: weight gain, metabolic syndrome (a constellation of physical changes like weight gain, high blood sugar, and unfavorable levels of cholesterol and other blood lipids that increase heart disease risk), and symptoms such as muscle spasms, tremor, and restlessness. (For a more complete list of side effects, see Table 2, page 23.)

One antipsychotic that is a special case is clozapine (Clozaril). This drug is sometimes effective when no other drug works. But it can cause a dangerous loss of infection-fighting white blood cells, and as many as half of people taking this drug develop metabolic syndrome. As a result, it is usually reserved as a treatment of last resort.

Anticonvulsants

Anticonvulsant drugs are named for their ability to treat seizure disorders (convulsions), but doctors have recognized that they are also useful for treating mania and stabilizing moods.

One such drug, valproate (Depakote), is not more effective than lithium, but the dose is easier to adjust, fewer blood tests are needed, and some people find its side effects easier to tolerate. Common side effects include nausea, sedation, and weight gain. It is not as toxic as lithium in overdose. However, doctors are cautious about prescribing this drug in young women because it may raise the risk of polycystic ovary syndrome, which can lead to infertility. In rare cases, valproate can cause severe problems, such as reduced liver function or low platelet counts.

Another anticonvulsant, lamotrigine (Lamictal), has proved useful in treating and preventing the depressive episodes that occur in bipolar disorder. It tends not to bring on a manic episode or cause rapid mood cycles. It can cause an uncommon but very dangerous rash if the dosage is increased quickly, so it has to be started according to a strict, slowly rising dosing schedule.

Carbamazepine (Tegretol) also may be helpful for treating and preventing depression in bipolar disorder. Dosing and blood levels are monitored carefully to avoid serious side effects, such as rashes, suppression of blood cell production, and liver damage.

Doctors prescribe other anticonvulsants, such as topiramate (Topamax) and gabapentin (Neurontin), on the theory that any member of the class might be helpful, but there is little evidence to support their use as mood stabilizers. Sometimes, treatment involves combinations of these medications.

Antidepressants

Because people with bipolar disorder are as likely to experience depression as they are to experience mania, doctors may also prescribe antidepressants, such as SSRIs and bupropion. One concern with using antidepressants to treat bipolar illness is that they might trigger a manic episode or cause a more rapid cycling of episodes.

A large-scale study didn't find that this was a problem, but it did call into question the effectiveness of combining an antidepressant and mood stabilizer. The Systematic Treatment Enhancement Program for Bipolar Disorder (STEP-BD), a multisite randomized clinical trial funded by the National Institute of Mental Health, found that while it was safe to add an antidepressant to a mood stabilizer—that is, it didn't trigger a switch to a manic episode—doing so didn't offer better results. Study participants received up to 26 weeks of treatment with either a mood stabilizer and an antidepressant (either bupropion or paroxetine) or a mood stabilizer and a placebo. The researchers found that 27% of those receiving the placebo improved significantly, compared with 23% of those taking the antidepressants. This study suggests that in many cases, sticking with a mood stabilizer may be a reasonable alternative to adding an antidepressant to the treatment.

Anti-anxiety medications

Anti-anxiety medications can relieve some of the uncomfortable symptoms of bipolar disorder—such as sleeplessness, jitteriness, racing thoughts, and overall worry and distress—that can occur mostly in mania but sometimes during depressive episodes, too. Benzodiazepines such as clonazepam (Klonopin) and lorazepam (Ativan) are often used for this purpose. Sedation is the main side effect, although it is often desirable in this case. However, many people with bipolar disorder have problems with dependency and addiction, so it's best to reserve these drugs for when symptoms are most intense. For more information on these medications, see Table 2 (page 23).

Managing side effects

It is hard to predict who will experience side effects from a given drug. That's why it is important for you to be aware of any changes in your body when you begin a new medication. Always tell your doctor about uncomfortable or worrisome side effects immediately.

You and your doctor can often alleviate side effects with a few simple steps. Here are some suggestions for dealing with common side effects of antidepressants:

Dry mouth. Drink a lot of water, chew sugarless gum, and brush your teeth frequently.

Constipation. Eat whole grains, bran cereal, prunes, and hearty servings of fruits and vegetables. Drink plenty of water.

Trouble urinating. If you have difficulty starting urination, your doctor may be able to adjust your medication to relieve this problem.

Dizziness. Sudden changes in position can lead to a sharp drop in blood pressure that causes dizziness. To counter this effect, move slowly when you rise from a chair or get out of bed. Also, drink plenty of fluids.

Daytime drowsiness. This problem usually occurs at the beginning of treatment and may not last long. In some cases, it may help to take medication at bedtime, but ask your doctor about this first. If you feel drowsy, don't drive or use heavy or dangerous equipment.

Trouble sleeping. Sleep often improves after a few weeks, but sometimes a mild sleep aid or a switch to another medication is necessary.

Nausea. Often, nausea disappears within a few weeks. It may help to take the drug shortly after a substantial meal.

Other symptoms such as agitation, headache, and sexual difficulties may improve with time, but if they don't, they warrant a conversation with your doctor.

Some side effects of medications are relatively easy to manage with a few simple steps. To handle others, your doctor may change your dose, but do not stop taking a drug without talking with your doctor.

Agitation. You might feel uncomfortably nervous or restless after you start taking a drug. Jittery feelings may pass within a few weeks. But in relatively rare cases, agitation will persist; if this happens to you, bring it to your doctor's attention because it may be an early sign of worsening depression or mania.

Headache. Headaches may come and go. Some persist, but they usually disappear within a few weeks.

Sexual difficulties. Sometimes sexual problems are transient or not related to the drug. Talk with your doctor about sexual problems that don't pass soon. (Also, see "Sexuality and SSRIs," page 26.)

If side effects continue to bother you, your doctor may change your dose, shift the time of day you take the medication, or split the daily dose into smaller amounts to be taken over the course of the day. Or he or she may recommend combining the drug with another one, switching to a different drug, or replacing drugs with therapy or other forms of treatment.

Take all medications as directed, and don't stop taking them abruptly without talking to your doctor.

Tapering off medication

If you find an antidepressant that lifts your dark mood and you aren't too troubled by its side effects, your doctor likely will renew the prescription indefinitely, figuring that it lowers the risk of relapse. But the side effects that may have been tolerable initially can

Table 3: Discontinuation symptoms or relapse?

DISCONTINUATION SYMPTOMS	RELAPSE SYMPTOMS
Emerge within one to four days of stopping the medication	Develop later and more gradually
Often include physical complaints not found in depression, such as dizziness, fatigue, headache, nausea; less commonly, electric-like shocks, hallucinations	Include symptoms of depression only
Disappear quickly if you take a dose of the antidepressant	Don't resolve with just one dose of antidepressant; improvement may take weeks
Resolve as the body readjusts	Continue and may worsen

become less acceptable over time. Or, because you feel better, you may think you no longer need the pills.

The decision to go off antidepressants should be considered thoughtfully and made with the support of your physician or therapist to make sure you're not stopping prematurely, risking a recurrence of depression. If you decide to quit, you and your physician should take steps to minimize or avoid the discontinuation symptoms that can occur if you stop taking these medications too abruptly.

Abrupt discontinuation can cause anxiety and low mood, which can look like a relapse of depression. Table 3 (above) includes some ways to distinguish discontinuation symptoms from a relapse. These symptoms are most common in people who abruptly stop taking SSRIs. The most frequent symptoms are dizziness, fatigue, headache, and nausea. Others include agitation, chills, sweating, muscle aches, and a runny nose. Some people experience "brain zaps"—a feeling that resembles an electric shock to your head—or a sensation some people describe as "brain shivers." Less commonly, people may experience auditory and visual hallucinations.

You can usually avoid these problems by slowly tapering the dose, which typically involves cutting down in increments, allowing two to six weeks or longer between dose reductions.

Your clinician can prescribe the appropriate pills and outline a plan for tapering your dose. In some cases, you can use a pill splitter to create smaller-dose pills, though be sure to check with your clinician or pharmacist to find out if your antidepressant can be split. You may also be able to use a liquid formulation for smaller dose adjustments.

Your tapering schedule will depend on which antidepressant you're taking, how long you've been taking it, your current dosage, and any symptoms you had during previous medication changes. Depending on how you respond to each dose reduction, you may want to taper more gradually, using smaller reductions, longer intervals between reductions, or both. If you experience discontinuation symptoms after a particular dose reduction, you may want to add back half the dose—or all of it—and continue from there with smaller reductions. There are no hard-and-fast rules, other than that the approach should be individualized. Some people can taper off an antidepressant in a matter of weeks, while others may take months.

Tapering off mood stabilizers and anticonvulsants (rather than abruptly stopping them) is also recommended, although there is no specific withdrawal syndrome to look out for. Instead, it is important for you and your doctor to monitor your condition in order to prevent relapse.

Psychotherapy

Depression can bring everything in your life—work, relationships, school, and even the most minor tasks—to a grinding halt, or, at the very least, gum up the works. The aim of psychotherapy is to relieve your symptoms and to help you manage your problems better and live the healthiest, most satisfying life you can.

By encouraging more constructive ways of thinking and acting, psychotherapy may help stave off future bouts of depression. Yet fewer than 20% of people on antidepressants undergo psychotherapy.

Three schools of psychotherapy—cognitive behavioral therapy, interpersonal therapy, and psychodynamic therapy—feature prominently in the treatment of depression. Which type of psychotherapy works best? There's no simple answer. Just as people respond differently to different drugs, you might do better with one type of therapy than with another. Many people find that a blended approach—one that draws on elements of different schools of psychotherapy—suits them best. In fact, many of the best trained therapists combine elements of these techniques. The descriptions in this chapter may inform your choice.

Cognitive behavioral therapy

The basic premise of cognitive behavioral therapy (CBT) is that your moods are directly related to your thinking patterns. Negative, dysfunctional thoughts—such as "I always screw up," "People don't like me," or "It's all my fault"—affect your sense of self. They can also influence your behavior (leading you to avoid social activities, for instance) and even your physical state (making you tired and sapping your energy). Together, negative thoughts and behaviors erode your self-esteem, leaving you vulnerable to depression.

A CBT-focused therapist aims to help you to recognize distorted, self-critical thoughts and then asks you to judge the truth of those assumptions. For example, a young man doing a new type of project at work may report that his supervisor corrected him. He feels self-critical, but also feels wounded, taking the interaction as evidence that the supervisor doesn't like him. The therapist might point out that it was the first time he had done this kind of work and then ask if he expected to do it perfectly the first time. If the man answers no, the therapist can then suggest that

10 questions to ask when choosing a therapist

Having good rapport with a therapist is the most important factor in determining the outcome of therapy. Pay attention to factors that can help you make a good match. Here are some questions to ask as you get to know a therapist:

1. What's your training (i.e., what certification or degrees do you hold), and what type of treatment or therapy do you practice?
2. How long have you worked in this field?
3. What kinds of treatment or therapy do you think might help me?
4. What are the advantages and disadvantages of the different approaches, including medication?
5. How does the treatment work?
6. What are the chances that treatment will succeed?
7. How soon should I start feeling better?
8. How will we assess my progress?
9. What should I do if I don't feel better?
10. How much will treatment cost?

These are not always easy questions to answer, and the therapist may not have the expertise to answer every one of them. Sooner rather than later, however, it would be good to know what kind of process you're embarking on. The therapist should have formal training and certification and be licensed in your state. In general, the therapist should be able to describe the merits and drawbacks of different types of treatment, including ones he or she doesn't offer. The therapist should also let you know how he or she will monitor your progress.

By taking note of the therapist's responses, you should get some sense of what the therapist is like and whether you will be able to establish a good working relationship.

the supervisor was providing correction to help the young man do his job well. Then they can talk about the possibility that he is overly sensitive to criticism and develop ways to better use his supervisor's input more constructively.

CBT also addresses the so-called automatic thoughts you may have in response to certain situations. They're automatic in that they're spontaneous and negative, not the result of reasoned thinking or logic. Often, they're stoked by defeatist or dysfunctional assumptions that guide how you view yourself, a particular situation, or the world around you. Examples of automatic thinking include

- always thinking the worst is going to happen
- always blaming yourself for bad outcomes
- exaggerating the negative aspects of something rather than the positive.

In treatment, the therapist will help you uncover underlying assumptions behind your thoughts. Once you recognize inaccurate assumptions, you can correct them by changing your perspective. Between sessions, your therapist may ask you to write down your negative thoughts in a journal and evaluate the situation that called them up.

Computer-based cognitive behavioral therapy (CCBT) for depression

It's not easy to find a good cognitive behavioral therapist. There may be too few in your area—or your insurance may offer limited coverage, making the expense too great. One stopgap may be computer-based tools that teach CBT principles. For example, the Australian-based Mood Gym (www.moodgym.com.au) is available for an annual fee that is less than the average cost of a single therapy session.

There is evidence that CCBT programs are helpful, but many users find them difficult to stick with. In fact, most participants in clinical trials of CCBT used them only once or twice. That may be because it's more difficult for people with depression to persist in the face of fatigue, impaired concentration, and feelings of hopelessness. Also, there is no actual therapeutic relationship with a mental health provider, which is thought to be a crucial ingredient of therapy.

In short, CCBT may turn out to be an effective treatment option, but it is far from proven.

Another CBT goal targets a common symptom of depression: not doing things you used to enjoy. Your therapist may encourage or help you to schedule enjoyable experiences, often with other people who can reinforce the enjoyment. Part of the process is to scrutinize any attitudes or choices that are preventing you from getting out and having fun, in part by breaking the process down into smaller steps. You rehearse new ways of coping with problems and practice social skills that can help wean you from thoughts and behaviors that make depression worse, such as isolating yourself.

Again, your therapist may encourage you to record your experience, taking a close look at the circumstances and how you felt. If it didn't go as planned, you might explore why and how you might change it in the future. Taking action toward a positive solution and goal can help you emerge from depression.

While some types of therapy are open-ended in terms of duration and goals, with CBT, you are more likely to work with the therapist to set targets and endpoints. In reality, the duration of therapy varies widely. You'll learn and practice skills, during which time your symptoms may ease. Many people say their symptoms improve within 12 weeks. More severe cases of depression may take longer to resolve. It can be helpful, after three to four months, to review your progress and goals with your therapist. As you gain confidence using your new skills, you may be ready to meet less frequently.

Another option is computer-based cognitive behavioral therapy (CCBT; at left), which may be more readily available and convenient, but still requires dedication to achieve results.

Although a wide range of people respond well to CBT, experts say that people who are most likely to benefit are those who are motivated, who believe that they can control events that happen to them, and who are capable of examining their own thoughts and feelings. Results from the landmark STAR*D study revealed that cognitive behavioral therapy is about as effective in treating depression as medication.

Interpersonal psychotherapy

Interpersonal psychotherapy concentrates on resolving interpersonal problems, both at work and at home.

Weekly sessions help you identify and practice ways to cope with recurring conflicts. Typically, therapy centers on one of four specific problems:

- grief over a recent loss
- a dispute with others about roles and social expectations
- the effect of a major life change, such as divorce or a new job
- social isolation.

Social role transitions are often major sources of stress and a frequent topic of discussion during therapy. Common examples are divorce, serious illness, job loss or retirement, and significant family changes, such as marriage, the birth of a child, moving, or a child leaving home. These situations involve new demands, the loss of a comforting routine, and sometimes separation from familiar people. If you've experienced this type of transition, you may have a tough time making the necessary changes and may need help adjusting to your new role.

The therapist will ask you to think about what has been lost and gained, to appreciate the reality of the losses, and to generate interest in the new opportunities. Therapists also try to defeat depression by helping you cultivate the self-confidence and support from others that will help you meet the demands of your new role.

If your depression has sprung from the death of a loved one, the therapist will try to help you move through the mourning process and revive your interest in life. Together, you can evoke memories of the lost person and talk about events surrounding the loss. He or she may ask you to explore any regrets or resentment against the person—and reassure you that these feelings are common and not a reason to feel guilty. You'll likely also be encouraged to consider alternatives to dwelling on the loss.

Therapy may also explore interpersonal conflict, which often leaves people demoralized by repetitive, frustrating disputes, usually with a relative or a romantic partner. The therapist may help you analyze the issues at stake, examine unstated assumptions that perpetuate the conflict, and make a plan, including rules for avoiding constant useless arguments. If all real communication has ceased and the relationship is dying, the therapist can help you make a break. Whatever plan you choose, your therapist may also encourage you to explore parallels in your previous relationships.

Three approaches to psychotherapy feature promimently in the treatment of depression. Just as people respond differently to different drugs, you might do better with one type of therapy over another.

A final focus is on interpersonal deficits; for example, if you have difficulty making any personal connections at all. The problem is not a change or crisis involving others, but the *absence* of significant events and relationships in your life. In this case, interpersonal therapists pay special attention to past accomplishments and hopeful moments that you may have forgotten or disregarded. Together, you and your therapist explore repetitive self-defeating patterns to identify possible parallels. Then the therapist tries to help you make what amounts to a social role transition by learning and practicing social skills, sometimes using methods borrowed from cognitive behavioral therapy.

Psychodynamic therapy

Psychodynamic therapy focuses on how life events, desires, and past and current relationships affect your feelings and the choices you make. It has roots in psychoanalysis, the long-term "talking cure" founded by Sigmund Freud.

Like psychoanalysis, psychodynamic therapy recognizes that the relationships and circumstances of early life continue to affect people as adults, that human behavior results from unconscious as well as conscious or rational motives, and that the act of talking about problems can help people find ways to solve them or at least to bear them.

The ingredients of good therapy

There are many different approaches to psychotherapy, but all good therapy shares some common elements. To start with, make sure that your therapist has a state license. While psychotherapy isn't always comfortable, you should feel reasonably at ease with your therapist. In the best case, the two of you will be, or will become, a good match. Of course, both of you must respect ethical and professional boundaries.

You can anticipate that therapy will provide some relief. Your therapist should not only offer reassurance and support, but also suggest a clear plan for how the therapy will proceed. You and your therapist should agree upon realistic goals early on. While well-defined problems might be addressed relatively quickly, you may need to approach more difficult problems from many angles, which will take longer.

Since mood disorders can have a broad influence on relationships, work, school, and leisure activities, therapy should address these areas when—or if possible before—they become a problem. Therapy isn't just for uncovering painful thoughts, although that's part of the work. Good therapy also addresses how you can adjust, adapt, or function better. And it helps you understand the nature of your distress. You should feel that your therapist approaches the important issues in your life in a way that's unique to your needs, not from a one-size-fits-all perspective. Pertinent issues springing from your culture, gender, and age, as well as individual differences, should shape the direction therapy takes.

If a doctor other than your therapist prescribes antidepressants for you, the two should communicate. If they don't do so on their own, you may want to encourage collaboration by asking your therapist and doctor to speak periodically. Your therapist ought to understand the medication portion of your treatment, encourage you to take medications as prescribed, and help monitor your response.

Although it's not uncommon to feel stuck at times, don't persist for months with that feeling. Some difficult problems take a long time to unravel, but you should sense progress. If you don't, it's a sign that the match between you and either the technique or the therapist isn't right. If four to six months have gone by and you don't feel better, raise the issue with your therapist, reevaluate the plan, and consider getting a second opinion.

Psychodynamic therapy relies on the personal connection between therapist and patient. This is called the therapeutic or working alliance. Together you and the therapist pay attention to thoughts and feelings that come up in the relationship. This can provide an opportunity to gain insight into aspects of experience that would be difficult to talk and think about otherwise. By encouraging you to say whatever comes to mind, the therapist also helps you understand yourself in new ways and to become more aware of a greater range of your thoughts, feelings, perceptions, and experiences.

In therapy, you'll be encouraged to explore and talk about your emotions—including those that are contradictory, threatening, or not immediately apparent. The focus is on using therapy to gain emotional, as well as intellectual, insight. Ideally, insight enables you to reconsider life patterns that once seemed inevitable or uncontrollable and leads to the identification of new choices and options. The insight may help you feel more ready to make changes.

Psychodynamic therapy also helps people recognize and overcome ingrained and often automatic ways by which they avoid coming to terms with distressing thoughts and feelings. Therapy may bring avoidance into high relief—such as when patients cancel therapy appointments, arrive late, or tiptoe around emotionally charged topics. A psychodynamic therapist may point out, for example, how such maneuvers often involve painful compromises between the wish to attend sessions and the fear of what may emerge during therapy. Psychodynamic therapy can help a person become more aware of these maneuvers, which are likely to manifest outside of therapy as well, with the aim of nurturing more flexible and adaptive ways of coping.

According to psychodynamic theory, early life experiences—especially with parents, caregivers, and other authority figures—shape present-day outlook and relationships. The goal is to explore how prior relationships and attachments may provide insight into current psychological problems. A psychodynamic therapist may work with you to identify recurring patterns in relationships, emotions, or behaviors (such as being drawn to a verbally abusive partner) to help you recognize these patterns. At other times you may already be painfully aware of self-defeating patterns, but need help to understand why they keep recurring and how to overcome psychological obstacles to making changes. The aim of this work is to give you greater freedom to direct your life.

While the duration of psychodynamic therapy can be open-ended, a variation called brief dynamic therapy is limited to a specific amount of time (for example, 12 to 20 weeks). Research suggests that the benefits of psychodynamic therapy not only endure after therapy ends, but increase with time. This suggests that insights you gain may equip you with psychological skills that grow stronger with use.

While psychodynamic therapy can be very effective, it is neither quick nor cheap. Insurance coverage may be limited, so out-of-pocket costs can be significant, depending on where you live.

Group, family, or couples therapy

Group, family, or couples therapy may also be part of a plan for treating depression or bipolar disorder. Group therapy draws on support generated from people in the group and uses the dynamics among them, along with the leader's help, to explore shared problems. Family therapy and couples therapy also delve into human interactions. Like group therapy, the aim is to define destructive patterns—such as scapegoating one family member or enabling a spouse's alcohol abuse—and replace them with healthier ones. These therapies can uncover hidden issues and establish lines of communication. Family therapy is useful when one person is struggling with emotions that evoke strong or unhelpful responses from other family members.

Other types of nondrug therapies: Activation, art, and animals

Some types of therapy are used in tandem with more established types of therapy. They include behavioral activation therapy, creative arts therapy, and animal-assisted therapy.

Behavioral activation therapy

Behavioral activation is a technique that helps depressed people do what they tend to avoid. Proponents of this type of therapy point out that depressed people tend to withdraw from stressful situations. They get some relief in the short run because they spare themselves the pain of confronting tough problems. But they also miss out on the rewards. For example, a depressed man may call in sick to avoid an unpleasant interaction with a coworker. In the long run, however, he misses out on the satisfaction that could come from getting his job done and earning a living. And avoidance leaves the original problem unchanged. Inaction just makes problems worse and deepens depression, so that getting out of bed in the morning becomes more difficult.

The therapist uses logic while taking special care not to make a vulnerable person feel shamed or blamed. Depression usually makes people withdraw from activities that could be pleasurable, so activity can help increase enjoyment in life and relieve depression. To encourage activities, therapists help their patients establish a realistic schedule or routine, encourage them to adhere to it, and gradually increase their activity. The therapist also tries to help people interrupt the circular, self-critical thinking associated with depressed feelings and pay attention to the present moment and actions that help them reach their long-term goals. Improving problem-solving skills makes up the third part of this type of therapy.

Unlike other types of therapy, behavioral activation therapy doesn't put a lot of emphasis on your thoughts or feelings. Instead, it focuses on simple

Working with animals such as dogs or horses can help some people cope with trauma. Animals are nonjudgmental and can provide you with a positive, close relationship.

strategies such as goal setting, problem solving, and attending to the task at hand, rather than on the overwhelming big picture. But it is not as simple as adopting an approach of "just do it" over "get in touch with your feelings." The answer, as usual, lies somewhere in the middle. You don't want a life of grinding through tasks without feeling anything. The strategy is to turn your attention away from thoughts and feelings that undermine your functioning, and toward thoughts that promote it. Practitioners of behavioral activation ask their patients to notice when they are dwelling on unproductive thoughts and focus instead on their immediate sensations. Once you begin to function better, it's easier and more useful to begin to examine your thoughts from a position of strength and understand why they were so negative in the first place.

Taking action is not easy for a depressed person to do on his or her own, but many individuals seem to respond to therapists' firm encouragement to do what's difficult. The potential benefits of this surprisingly uncomplicated approach gained some traction from a 2016 study in *The Lancet*. The findings suggested that behavioral activation therapy is just as effective as CBT, though it costs less. An editorial accompanying the study proposed that behavioral activation therapy derives its benefit from emphasizing activities that a person values and finds meaningful. This allows depressed individuals to push back against adversity and despair. Furthermore, the approach offers cost savings because the treatment can be provided by individuals with less training.

Creative arts therapy

Expressive or creative arts therapy is based on the idea that creative pursuits are meaningful activities that can enhance any individual's sense of well-being. Although there isn't a great deal of research on the effectiveness of these approaches, they may appeal to people who are drawn to creative forms of expression. And you do not need any particular talent in any of these disciplines—only a willingness to participate.

Art therapy uses the creative process of making visual art—drawing, painting, sculpting, and other art forms—as therapy. The self-expression it fosters is thought to help people resolve conflicts and problems, lower their stress, boost their self-esteem and awareness, and gain insight into their problems. For more information, contact the American Art Therapy Association (www.arttherapy.org).

Music therapy interventions can be active (making music) or receptive (listening to music). In addition to easing stress and anxiety and boosting your mood and motivation, music therapy helps people explore and express their feelings. The American Music Therapy Association (www.musictherapy.org) offers more information.

Dance therapy is grounded in the concept of the mind-body connection and uses movement to improve self-esteem, body image, and communication skills. More information is available from the American Dance Therapy Association (www.adta.org).

Expressive writing involves the act of writing about feelings and thoughts that arise from a traumatic or stressful life experience. For a fuller description, see "Expressive writing," page 46.

Animal-assisted therapy

Working with animals such as horses, dogs, or cats can help some people cope with trauma, develop empathy, and communicate better. Companion animals are sometimes introduced to hospitals, psychiatric wards, nursing homes, and other places where they may bring comfort and have a mild therapeutic effect. Animal-assisted therapy has also been used as an added therapy for children with mental disorders.

There's evidence that having a pet can boost your mood. In one study, people given a dog or cat reported improved psychological well-being and self-esteem when questioned six to 10 months after acquiring their furry companions. Surveys suggest that pet owners are less likely to be depressed, anxious, and lonely. Several possible reasons could account for this:

- Pets increase social interaction. You're more likely to strike up a conversation with a stranger if a dog is around.
- Petting, stroking, and hugging a pet lower your stress levels, which can promote emotional health.
- Pets are affectionate and nonjudgmental and can provide you with a positive, close relationship—all of which lessens anxiety and stress. ■

Brain and nerve stimulation therapies

Brain and nerve stimulation therapies activate the brain with electricity or magnetism. They are usually recommended for people who haven't responded to other therapies for depression.

The oldest one, electroconvulsive therapy (ECT), is a well-established yet sometimes feared treatment for hard-to-treat cases of depression. But it has evolved into a relatively safe and potentially life-saving procedure for people who are severely depressed. Two other treatments, repetitive transcranial magnetic stimulation (rTMS) and vagus nerve stimulation (VNS), have been in use for several years as alternative ways to modulate brain activity. But neither has the proven track record of ECT, and very few people receive these treatments.

If you haven't been able to obtain relief from depression using the usual treatments, the doctor may recommend a type of therapy that stimulates the brain or vagus nerve with electricity or magnetism.

Electroconvulsive therapy

Also known as electroshock or shock therapy, electroconvulsive therapy (ECT) may evoke frightening images, but the procedure has been refined and improved since its introduction in the 1930s. Today, it remains one of the most effective treatments for severe depression, with response rates of 80% to 90% for people with major depression. ECT may also be used to treat mania when a person fails to respond to other treatments.

Despite its effectiveness, doctors usually reserve ECT for situations in which several drugs have failed. Before deciding on this treatment, you should receive a detailed explanation of what to expect, which may include watching videos of the procedure or speaking to others who've had ECT.

First, you receive general anesthesia and other drugs that prevent the outward signs of the seizure. Then the doctor places electrodes on your scalp and administers an electric current in a brief pulse that causes a seizure. The procedure takes a few minutes, after which you are roused from the anesthesia.

It's the seizure (not the electricity) that is thought to provide relief. Seizures are thought to alter brain chemistry and function in ways that ease depression. Animal studies have shown that ECT, like antidepressants, may spur the growth of new neurons.

People typically receive six to 12 treatments over several weeks. Those who respond usually improve gradually over the course of treatment. Because the response may be faster than with medications, ECT can be a good option for severely depressed people who may be at very high risk for suicide.

Some people lose memories of events that occurred just before or soon after the treatment. Few people have persistent memory problems after completing the therapy. However, ECT may exaggerate problems in people already having memory trouble. Some people feel a bit sedated or tired on the day of the procedure, or they might have a mild headache or nausea. These symptoms might come from the anesthesia rather than ECT itself.

About half of people treated for severe depression with ECT experience a relapse of their depression, and this may be even higher with so-called double depression (major depression plus persistent depressive disorder). Taking antidepressants and mood stabilizers may help prevent relapses.

Some people receive maintenance ECT about once a month.

Repetitive transcranial magnetic stimulation

Repetitive transcranial magnetic stimulation (rTMS) uses magnetic fields to alter brain function, possibly improving connections between neurons and changing how regions of the brain interact to influence mood. It is offered to people who have failed to get better after at least one, but usually many other, treatments for depression. People with seizure disorders and individuals who have metallic implants (such as cochlear implants or pacemakers) should not receive rTMS.

During the treatment, you sit in what looks like a dentist's chair while the technician holds a device containing a magnetic coil over your scalp. The device produces a series of strong magnetic pulses, which penetrate to a depth of about 2 to 3 centimeters into the brain, setting up a weak electrical current that is believed to change the activity of neurons in certain brain regions. You remain awake and may feel a slight knocking or tapping from the pulses.

A session usually lasts 30 to 60 minutes, and is usually done once a day, five days a week for four to six weeks. Following this course of treatment, maintenance therapy may be given on a less frequent basis. The most common side effects—headaches, scalp discomfort, or facial twitching—are mild. Seizures during treatment are possible but rare.

There are other drawbacks. The benefits of rTMS are modest. Most health insurance plans do not cover rTMS, and each session costs up $300, which means a typical course of treatment may run $7,500 or more.

Vagus nerve stimulation

Vagus nerve stimulation (VNS) was originally developed as a way to treat epilepsy, but researchers noticed that the therapy also seemed to alleviate depression. The treatment involves implanting in the upper chest a pacemaker-like device that delivers regular pulses of electricity to the vagus nerve. This nerve, which extends from the brain to the belly, connects to brain areas thought to be involved in mood regulation. The pulses last 30 seconds every five minutes and appear to alter levels of serotonin and other neurotransmitters linked to mood.

The implantation surgery involves risks of bleeding and infection, but the most common side effects of the treatment itself are cough and neck pain. Many people also find that their voice becomes hoarse while the device is stimulating the vagus nerve.

Although the FDA approved VNS based on early research showing the treatment was safe and effective, subsequent studies have found only weak evidence showing a benefit from this therapy.

The cost—estimated at over $20,000 for the surgery and device—is unlikely to be covered by insurance.

Self-care and alternative treatments for depression

About four in 10 Americans—and as many as half of those with mental health problems—use dietary supplements or other types of complementary or alternative medicines in any given year. Alternative or complementary therapies probably won't cure your depression on their own. But some self-help strategies—especially getting regular exercise and eating right—may help lift your mood. Of course, it can be tough, even under the best of circumstances, to find the time to exercise, choose and cook healthy foods, and get enough sleep. It's far more difficult when you're struggling with the apathy and melancholy of depression. But taking good care of yourself is important for both your physical and mental health, and it brings an added benefit: practicing healthy habits can help you feel that you're gaining control of your life again.

These strategies may help in different ways. Eating a healthful diet, along with taking selected dietary supplements, may provide a helpful boost to your medication regimen. Other approaches, such as mindfulness meditation and expressive writing, can help restore a sense of calm and provide emotional stability. Any or all of these treatments are worth trying in addition to whatever you're working on with your doctor. In fact, the practice guidelines for treating depression, published by the American Psychiatric Association, include information on such treatments. That means your provider is likely to be familiar with them and should be able to offer advice.

Exercise

How you treat your body affects your mind and your level of happiness. Unfortunately, many people's lifestyles include a natural depressant: being sedentary. Humans have evolved to be physically active, and exercise has been shown to enhance well-being and help prevent or reduce anxiety and depression. In fact, the American Psychiatric Association practice guidelines for depression also acknowledge the importance of exercise and a healthy lifestyle to the brain's ability to regulate mood.

Although it is difficult to ramp up your activity level, especially when you're depressed, it is probably the one thing a person can do that has almost universal positive effects and few (if any) side effects. The research on the benefits of exercise for mood is fairly robust, showing that regular exercise can improve mood in people with mild to moderate depression and may even play a supporting role in treating severe depression. A Cochrane Collaboration review of more than 30 randomized, controlled studies found exercise to be about as effective as cognitive behavioral therapy or antidepressant medications in reducing symptoms.

For example, a study that assigned 156 older adults with major depression to one of three interventions—an aerobic exercise program, the SSRI sertraline (Zoloft), or both—found that at the four-month mark, 60% to 70% of the people in all three groups no longer had major depression. In fact, group scores on two rating scales of depression were essentially the same. The major difference between the groups was that the participants taking sertraline had the fastest initial response. However, in a follow-up study, those who exercised regularly for six months after the end of the first trial were less likely to relapse, regardless of which treatment group they were in originally.

This suggests that for those who have mild to moderate depression and need or wish to avoid drug treatment, exercise might be an acceptable substitute for antidepressants.

While it hasn't been established exactly how much exercise or what kind is needed, aerobic exercise and resistance training both appear to help—and a combination of the two seems most effective. As for how much is needed, an old exercise maxim is probably applicable: some is always better than none, but more is better than some. For example, one small study in the Cochrane review found that people who exercised three to five days a week had a greater reduction in depression than those who only exercised once a week. The Physical Activity Guidelines for Americans recommend that all adults get 150 minutes of moderate aerobic exercise per week (30 minutes five days a week) plus two strength training sessions. Together, such a regimen offers many health benefits, such as lowering blood pressure, protecting against heart disease and type 2 diabetes, reducing your risk for various types of cancer, keeping bones strong and healthy, and helping you maintain your vitality and independence in later years.

How does exercise relieve depression? For some years, researchers thought mood improvements came mainly from the increased release of endorphins (small molecules naturally produced by the body in response to pain) into the bloodstream. While that may be a factor, especially after an intense workout, it's probably not what causes enduring improvement in depressive symptoms.

Exercise turns out to have many benefits for the brain. It improves blood flow, bringing more oxygen and glucose for energy to neurons. It promotes a reduction in chronic inflammation in the brain. It increases the production of many small molecules known as neurotrophic factors that support the growth, survival, and healthy functioning of neurons—and even prompts the production of new neurons (neurogenesis) in key brain areas that govern mood. It seems to improve functioning of the body's stress system, too, boosting the production of helpful "neurosteroids." All of these changes make the brain work better, improving both mood and intellectual capacity. The story of exercise is thus getting more complex and interesting.

Diet

Sweet, salty, and fatty foods may make you happy while you're eating them, but a regular diet of junk food can be a downer. Several studies have linked a poor diet with depression. One found that the more fast food (hamburgers, sausages, and pizza) a person ate, the greater the risk of depression. A similar trend was seen among those who ate store-bought baked goods, such as muffins, doughnuts, and croissants.

On the flip side, a healthy diet appears to enhance your mood.

The burgeoning field of nutritional psychiatry focuses the connection between food and your mood—especially how your diet affects the billions of bacteria that live in your gut, known as your gut microbiome. About 95% of your serotonin is produced in your gastrointestinal tract, and your gastrointestinal tract is lined with a hundred million neurons. So it just makes sense that your digestive system helps guide your emotions. Your gut microbiome protects the lining of your intestines, shielding it against toxins and "bad" bacteria. The bacteria also improve how well you absorb nutrients from your food, tamp down chronic low-grade inflammation, and activate neural pathways between the gut and the brain.

An analysis that pooled data from 11 studies found that diets rich in olive oil, fish, fruits and vegetables, nuts, and legumes (peas and beans) were linked to a lower risk of depression. One of those studies identified and compared two dietary patterns in more than 3,400 middle-aged men and women. The "whole food" dietary pattern featured piles of vegetables, fruits, and fish, and the "processed food" pattern was loaded with sweetened desserts, fried food, processed meat, refined grains (foods made with white flour), and high-fat dairy products. After five years of follow-up, the participants filled out a depression questionnaire. Based on the scores, the study's authors concluded that a whole-food dietary pattern seems to help shield people from depression, whereas a diet based on processed food appears to raise the risk—although it is also possible that people with depression choose less healthy foods.

The evidence is still limited, but there's no harm in trying the following tips for improving your gut health, which may also improve your mood:

- Eat whole foods and avoid packaged or processed foods, which are high in food additives and preservatives that disrupt the healthy bacteria in the gut.
- Instead of vegetable or fruit juice, consider increasing your intake of fresh fruits and vegetables. Frozen fruits without added sugars or additives are a good choice too.
- Eat enough fiber and include whole grains and legumes in your diet.
- Include probiotic-rich foods such as plain yogurt without added sugars.
- To reduce sugar intake at breakfast, add cinnamon to plain yogurt with berries, or to oatmeal or chia pudding.
- Adding fermented foods such as kefir (unsweetened), sauerkraut, or kimchi can be helpful to maintain a healthy gut.
- Eat a balance of seafood and lean poultry, and less red meat each week.
- Add a range of colorful fresh fruits and vegetables to your diet, and consider choosing certain organic produce.

In multiple studies, diets rich in vegetables, fruits, nuts, legumes, and olive oil have been linked to a lower risk of depression.

Dietary supplements

Many people with depression are curious about dietary supplements as an alternative or addition to traditional medications. In 2016, a review in the *American Journal of Psychiatry* identified several supplements that seem to boost the effectiveness of antidepressant drugs: omega-3 fatty acids, S-adenosylmethionine (SAMe), vitamin D, and methylfolate. The findings were based on 40 studies published between 1960 and 2015 that examined the effectiveness of a dozen different supplements in people with depression who were also taking antidepressants. Unfortunately, there is no evidence that taking a complex array of nutraceuticals (a "shotgun approach") is useful for treating depression. In fact, according to a recent study, it was *less* effective than a placebo.

Omega-3 fatty acids. These fatty acids are abundant in coldwater fish such as salmon, mackerel, herring, and albacore tuna. The two main omega-3s, EPA and DHA, are thought to affect neurotransmitters involved in mood regulation, in addition to dampening inflammation. They are widely available in capsule form; the latest evidence suggests that supplements containing EPA appear to be the most beneficial, taken daily in doses of 1 to 2 grams in addition to an antidepressant. Avoid higher doses, as they may increase risk of gastrointestinal bleeding and stomach upset.

S-adenosylmethionine (SAMe). Made naturally in the body, SAMe boosts production of several neurotransmitters involved in regulating mood. Adults may benefit from 400 to 1,600 milligrams (mg) per day, although some people will need to take 3,000 mg per day to alleviate symptoms. Combining SAMe with an antidepressant is safe, for the most part, but in very rare cases may cause serotonin syndrome—a potentially deadly complication that causes agitation, anxiety, confusion, nausea, vomiting, and palpitations. SAMe can also trigger mania in people with bipolar disorder.

Vitamin D. The brain has receptors for this vitamin in some key areas involved in depression, such as the prefrontal cortex. Vitamin D has been shown to increase the expression of genes that encode for a precursor of dopamine and norepinephrine. There is no established dose of vitamin D for depression.

Methylfolate. L-methylfolate, a form of the B vitamin folic acid, has shown some promise as an adjunct to antidepressants. It is currently sold as a patented supplement called Deplin. However, the cost is high and the benefit uncertain, so many clinicians consider methylfolate a low-priority option for treating depression.

Two supplements not named in the review also have some evidence behind them:

St. John's wort. This herbal supplement, produced from an extract of the plant *Hypericum perforatum*, may be an alternative to medication for children and adolescents. As an alternative to medication, it may also help adults with mild to moderate symptoms of depression, but it is unlikely to help those with severe symptoms. Physicians strongly warn against taking it with an antidepressant, as the combination can cause serotonin syndrome—which, as mentioned above, is a rare but potentially deadly complication that causes agitation, anxiety, confusion, nausea, vomiting, and palpitations. It can also reduce the effectiveness of many drugs, so check with your doctor before using it. Adults can take 900 to 1,800 mg in a 24-hour period, ideally divided into two or three capsules taken over the course of a day.

N-acetyl cysteine. This amino acid derivative can help depressive symptoms in bipolar disorder. Studies have used 2,000 mg per day, added to standard bipolar disorder treatment.

Note that because all of these products are classified as dietary supplements, they can be sold without a prescription and without FDA approval. As a result, their effects have not been scrutinized as rigorously as those of medications approved by the FDA. In addition, supplements do not always contain the dose marked on the label, making their effects harder to predict. Finally, be sure to tell your doctor about any supplements you want to try, because some of them have interactions with prescription medications.

Mindfulness meditation

In our busy world, multitasking is a way of life. We fold the laundry while keeping one eye on the kids and another on the television. We pay the bills, munch on a snack, and listen to a spouse complain

By learning to focus on the present moment through meditation or other mindfulness practices, many people find they worry less.

about a work project, all at the same time. But in the rush to accomplish necessary tasks, we often lose our connection with the present moment. We sprint through daily activities without being truly attentive to what we're doing and how we're feeling.

Mindfulness, which is at the heart of many spiritual practices, is an antidote to this. It is the practice of focusing attention on the present and becoming more comfortable with one's thoughts and feelings without too much self-criticism. And that—many physicians and therapists believe—can be a powerful therapeutic tool. By learning to focus on the here and now, many people who practice mindfulness find that they are less likely to get caught up in worries about the future or regrets over the past. They are also more able to appreciate simple everyday experiences and savor the sights, sounds, and tastes they enjoy.

Mindfulness is often learned through meditation, a method of regulating your attention by focusing on your breathing, a phrase, or an image. Meditation has distinct effects on the brain and, in turn, the rest of the body. It appears to calm the stress response (see "How stress affects the body," page 6), and reduces the risk associated with conditions such as high blood pressure, chronic pain, sleep problems, and gastrointestinal difficulties. It is also associated with improvement in markers of inflammation.

In the brains of experienced meditators, researchers see beneficial changes in regions that govern attention, the regulation of emotion, and the processing of ideas about the self. Some brain changes are associated with stronger focus and an enhanced ability to choose when and how to react to thoughts and feelings that emerge. Over all, one can see a boost in equanimity and sense of well-being in those who meditate regularly.

Another goal of mindfulness is to facilitate personal change—much the same goal as psychotherapy. During mindfulness meditation, you attend to distracting thoughts and sensations that may occur. Ronald Siegel, a clinical psychologist and co-editor of the book *Mindfulness and Psychotherapy*, points out that people with low moods or anxiety often are struggling against something—resisting sadness, fear, loss, or pain. Recognizing and accepting your feelings and thoughts gives you a chance to be less reactive. Perspective on the nature of the mind facilitates your changing negative patterns of thoughts and action.

Mindfulness exercises to try

Here are two mindfulness exercises you can try on your own.

1 A meditation exercise

Sit on a straight-backed chair or cross-legged on the floor. Focus on an aspect of your breathing, such as the sensations of air flowing into your nostrils and out of your mouth, or your belly rising and falling as you inhale and exhale.

Once you've narrowed your concentration in this way, begin to widen your focus. Become aware of sounds, sensations, and your ideas. Embrace and consider each without judgment. If your mind starts to race, return your focus to your breathing. Then expand your awareness again. Take as much time as you like—one minute or five or 10—whatever you're comfortable with. Experts in mindfulness meditation note that the practice is most useful if you can commit to a regular meditation schedule.

2 Practicing awareness in daily life

Another approach to mindfulness, sometimes called "open awareness," can help you stay in the present and truly participate in your life. You can choose any task or moment to practice mindfulness. Whether you are eating, showering, walking, touching a partner, or playing with a child or grandchild, attending to these three points will help:

- Start by breathing deeply. Breathe in through your nose, allowing the air to expand downward. Let your abdomen expand fully. Now breathe out through your mouth. Stay aware of each inhalation and exhalation.
- Proceed with the task or activity at hand slowly and with full attention.
- Engage your senses fully so that you remain aware of every sensation.

In 1979, Jon Kabat-Zinn, a psychologist and professor of medicine at the University of Massachusetts Medical School, established a successful stress reduction program based on principles of mindfulness meditation. Psychologists Zindel Segal, John Teasdale, and Mark Williams applied the principles developed by Kabat-Zinn and his colleagues to the treatment of depression. Called mindfulness-based cognitive therapy (MBCT), it combines mindfulness techniques with cognitive behavioral therapy. Like any meditation practice, it takes time to yield results. Also, the longer and more faithfully you practice, the greater the effects. Particularly as a drug-free intervention, it is promising. The essentials of the program can be found in a book and companion CD of guided meditations they published with Kabat-Zinn, called *The Mindful Way through Depression.*

MBCT seems particularly useful for helping to prevent recurrences of depression, according to a 2016 study in *JAMA Psychiatry*. Researchers pooled data from nine separate studies involving more than 1,200 people. All had taken part in studies that compared MBCT with at least one different therapy. During the 60-week follow-up period, people treated with MBCT were less likely to experience a relapse of their depression compared with those who had other treatments. What's more, the benefits were strongest in people who had the most severe depression.

If mindfulness meditation appeals to you, ask your therapist how best to use it. As a first step, you can try one of the exercises suggested in this report (see "Mindfulness exercises to try," page 45).

Expressive writing

Expressive writing, a technique that involves writing about thoughts and feelings that arise from a traumatic or stressful life experience, may help some people cope with the emotional fallout of stress, trauma, and unexpected life events.

Studies of expressive writing have included all sorts of permutations: for example, participants writing for 10 to 30 minutes at a time, for one to five days—or weekly for four weeks. The standard format involves writing for a specified period each day about a particularly stressful or traumatic experience. Participants usually write nonstop while exploring their innermost thoughts and feelings without inhibition (and the writing samples remain confidential for that reason). They may also use the exercise to understand how the traumatic event may revive memories of other stressful events.

To date, studies of the mental health effects of expressive writing have demonstrated that the practice

- eased depression among women who were victims of domestic violence
- reduced stigma-related stress in gay men
- helped chronically stressed caregivers of older adults
- improved the grades of anxious test takers who wrote briefly about their thoughts and feelings before an important exam.

Why might writing help? The act of thinking about an experience seems to be important. Writing helps you organize your thoughts—and the act of creating a narrative gives meaning to a traumatic experience. It may also be an intellectual exercise that creates some distance or perspective and enables you to better regulate the emotions associated with difficult challenges. Finally, when you open up privately about an event that troubles you, you may be more likely to talk with others about it—suggesting that writing leads indirectly to reaching out for social support that can aid healing.

Timing also matters. A few studies have found that people who write about a traumatic event immediately after it occurs may actually feel worse after expressive writing, possibly because they are reinforcing the experience rather than reflecting on it. As such, experts advise clinicians and their patients to wait at least one or two months after a traumatic event before trying this technique.

Even with these caveats, however, expressive writing is such an easy, low-cost technique—much like taking a good brisk walk—that it may be worth trying to see if it helps.

Suicide: Understanding the risk

Most people who die by suicide have mood problems, but what triggers this irrevocable step varies from person to person. Suicide may stem from intense feelings of anger, despair, hopelessness, or panic. Sometimes it's carried out under the sway of a highly distorted or psychotic idea.

At other times, a major life change can put someone at a higher risk for suicide. Here are examples of events that can abruptly increase the risk:

- an episode of depression, psychosis, or anxiety
- a recent significant loss, such as the death of a spouse or the loss of a job
- loss of social support—for example, because of a move or when a close friend relocates
- a personal crisis or life stress, especially one that increases a sense of isolation, is humiliating, or leads to a loss of self-esteem, such as a separation or divorce
- an illness or medication that triggers a change in mood
- exposure to the suicidal behaviors of others, such as friends, peers, or celebrities.

These stresses do not typically lead to suicide. Suicide is rare, which is fortunate. But its rarity also makes it impossible to predict who will take his or her own life. By providing treatment and support, however, it is possible to significantly reduce the risk that someone will follow such a course of action.

Experts observe that suicide is more common among certain groups of people. Factors that raise concern include the following.

Family history of suicide. People with a biological relative who has died by suicide have a risk that is much higher than average. Among identical twins, who share all their genes, if one twin has committed suicide, 13% of the surviving twins take their own lives. That compares with less than 1% among fraternal twins. This vulnerability may be the product of genes that predispose a person toward an impulsive temperament. Family histories of mental illness or violence also boost the risk of suicide.

Access to guns. In the United States, more than half of all suicides are by gunshot. Studies have found having a gun in the home makes suicide more likely. For example, a 2016 study in the *American Journal of Public Health* correlated gun ownership and rates of suicides involving firearms over a 32-year period. For men, the rates ranged from a low of 4.2 firearm-assisted suicides per 100,000 men in Massachusetts (the state with the second lowest gun ownership in the country) to a high of 26.1 per 100,000 men in Wyoming (the state with the highest gun ownership). That's a sixfold difference. Other research shows that in any individual home, the risk might be as much as two to 10 times greater, depending on how the gun is stored and the ages of those living in the home.

Suicides in the United States

Reliable statistics on suicide aren't easy to compile because reporting is not always candid, and records are not always thorough. Still, here is a look at the most recent figures available:

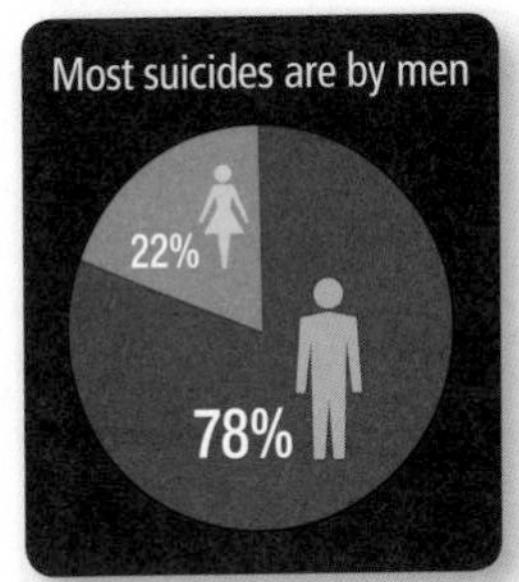

- In the United States, suicide is the second leading cause of death in youths and young adults ages 10 to 34, the fourth leading cause in adults ages 35 to 54, and the 10th leading cause of death over all.
- Suicide rates are roughly 3.5 times higher in men than women, but 1.4 times as many women attempt suicide.
- Between 1999 and 2016, suicide rates increased by more than 30% in 25 states.
- For every suicide death, there are an estimated 25 attempted suicides.

Sources: Centers for Disease Control and Prevention; National Institute of Mental Health.

It's not just adults who are at risk. Children also use guns to kill themselves; 82% of these suicides involve guns at home, mostly stored unlocked. When children attempt suicide, 90% succeed in killing themselves when guns are used, as compared with 5% with other means. These deaths are hard to prevent because young people often act impulsively and there may be no early warning signs, such as expression of suicidal thoughts or statements like "I wish I'd never been born."

Can antidepressants trigger suicide?

There have been reports that selective serotonin reuptake inhibitors (SSRIs) increase the frequency of suicidal thinking. But the possibility that SSRIs increase the risk of actual suicide is very controversial—and instances appear to be rare.

Since 2004, the FDA has required drug manufacturers to include a warning about this risk on package inserts of all commonly used antidepressants. In 2007, the FDA expanded the warning to state that there was an increased risk of suicidal thoughts and behaviors in young adults, ages 18 to 24, during the first two months of treatment. However, the labels also point to two reassuring aspects of the research:

- Taking antidepressants poses no increased risk for adults over age 24.
- Adults over age 65 who take antidepressants have a lower risk of suicide and suicidal thoughts, and there is growing evidence that this is true for most age groups.

Subsequent research confirms that when compared with a placebo, all antidepressants may trigger suicidal thinking or self-destructive behavior in a small number of people who are sensitive to this effect.

As antidepressant use falls, suicides rise

Not only is there little evidence that links actual teen suicides to antidepressant use, several studies suggest that just the opposite is true—that antidepressant treatment reduces the risk of suicide in young people.

A 2014 study in *BMJ* tracked antidepressant use among 2.5 million young people between 2000 and 2010. After the FDA's warnings in 2003 and 2004, use of commonly prescribed antidepressants like fluoxetine (Prozac), sertraline (Zoloft), and others fell by 30% in teenagers and 25% in young adults. During that same period, suicide attempts rose by 22% in teens and 34% in young adults. The researchers concluded that the decrease in antidepressant use may have left many depressed young people without appropriate treatment, leading to the increase in suicide attempts. In general, prior to 2003, suicide rates for adolescents were dropping.

Why the increase in suicidal thoughts in some people?

Researchers are still trying to ascertain why antidepressants might increase suicidal thoughts in certain young people. Adolescents do tend to be more self-destructive and impulsive than people in other age groups, and depression itself increases the risk of suicide. So this is a group that has more suicidal thinking than average to start with. It's therefore hard to sort out how to interpret suicidal thinking when it occurs after a depressed adolescent starts an antidepressant. Does the antidepressant cause the thinking, or is it a coincidence? Would the adolescent have had the suicidal thinking with or without the drug?

No one knows how an antidepressant might intensify suicidal thinking or a tendency toward self-harm. A decades-old theory is that severely depressed people may recover the energy to act on suicidal thoughts before their mood improves or hope returns. An antidepressant may trigger a first

Antidepressants have been linked to suidical thoughts in a small number of people ages 24 and younger.

episode of mania in a vulnerable person. Or it may cause a spike in irritability, anxiety, or restlessness to a degree that is unbearable. None of these ideas is proven.

The need for close monitoring

The way to diminish risk is to have regular follow-ups and close monitoring by a doctor. With your doctor, pay special attention any time you are starting a new drug or if you are changing the dose—either increasing or decreasing it. Watch for signs that the depression is worsening or that suicidal thoughts or behaviors have emerged. Such monitoring is particularly important in the first month or two of treatment with a new medicine.

If you feel worse after beginning treatment or if you develop uncomfortable symptoms (like anxiety or restlessness), let your doctor know right away. The same advice holds true for children: if your child's symptoms seem to worsen or you notice any signs of suicidal thinking or behavior, contact the child's doctor immediately.

There is a widely held belief that someone serious about suicide will find an equally effective means if a gun isn't available, but data do not support this idea. In fact, studies indicate that suicides are frequently impulsive, meaning the time between deciding to end one's life and attempting the act took just a few minutes to an hour. The stressors that often lead to a suicidal crisis—for example, a job loss or the end of a romantic relationship—are temporary, and experts have found that the most intense and immediate psychological pain passes relatively quickly—and so does the urge to end one's life.

Researchers in Switzerland, publishing in the *American Journal of Psychiatry*, reported on the change in suicide rates that came after the size of that country's army was cut in half. Swiss soldiers keep their firearms at home, so this change quickly cut the number of firearms kept in Swiss homes. There was a parallel decrease in the suicide rate among men 18 to 43 years of age (the age group that does military service). Importantly, the evidence shows that people did not turn to methods other than firearms to commit suicide.

Many public health experts have argued for policies that would reduce gun-related deaths. For example, you can promote gun safety by locking up any guns in the house or installing trigger locks. But the safest house is still one without guns. The American Academy of Pediatrics advises removing guns and ammunition from the house if a child might be depressed or suicidal. The same recommendation would hold true for adults.

Substance abuse. The combination of depression and alcohol or drug use can be deadly because these substances can erase inhibitions and anxiety that might help keep suicide at bay. Or, as the more soothing effects of such self-medication wear off, hopelessness may take hold.

Previous attempts. When someone has survived one or more attempted suicides, friends and relatives may take further attempts less seriously. But people with a history of attempted suicide are more likely to commit suicide than those who haven't tried it before. The National Institute of Mental Health warns, "Most suicide attempts are expressions of extreme distress, not harmless bids for attention." Therefore, suicidal behavior should always be taken seriously.

Setting affairs in order. Individuals who have decided on suicide may sort out their finances, give away mementos, or call or visit loved ones. People who have been agitated or depressed may seem calmer and happier. But rather than being a sign of returning health, this shift may stem from their relief at having made a final decision.

Get help NOW

If you need help or are having suicidal thoughts, call 800-273-TALK (800-273-8255). This National Suicide Prevention Lifeline service is free and available 24 hours a day. The Lifeline also offers an online chat service, at https://suicidepreventionlifeline.org/chat.

Alternatively, you can call 911, or go to your local emergency room.

Help is available

If you or a loved one feels suicidal, seek help:

- Talk with your doctor or a mental health professional. Very often, treatment eases or entirely eliminates suicidal urges. In some cases, hospitalization is necessary until a sense of equilibrium returns.
- Call the National Suicide Prevention Lifeline at 800-273-TALK (800-273-8255) or a local hotline and speak with a crisis counselor.
- Discuss your feelings with trusted family members, friends, or religious advisers who can assist you in getting help.

Living with depression: Strategies for success

Finding good treatment for depression—whether major depression, persistent depressive disorder, or bipolar disorder—can feel like running in a track meet. Just when you think you are getting somewhere, you find yourself facing a series of hurdles. Dealing with the stigma of depression, sorting through insurance and financial issues, choosing the right treatment, and sticking with it despite side effects and other challenges can seem like insurmountable obstacles, but they can be overcome.

Overcoming stigma

Because we cannot see what is going on inside the brain, depression and other mental health problems historically have been shrouded in mystery and even fear. Moreover, many people still mistakenly view symptoms of depression or the desire to get treatment as signs of weak character, lack of fortitude, or an inability to pull oneself up by the bootstraps.

One of the worst results of stigma is that people suffering from depression may feel shame about their condition and be reluctant to seek treatment, leaving them stuck on a destructive course that could lead to more pain, a poorer quality of life, and, in some cases, suicide. According to the Substance Abuse and Mental Health Services Administration, stigma associated with mental illness is one of the primary reasons why people don't seek mental health treatment.

Despite the devastating effects stigma still has on many people, surveys suggest that over the past decade, seeking mental health treatment has become more acceptable and that perceived stigma associated with seeking treatment has also declined.

Several developments may help explain this shift. First, public awareness about mental illness is growing, partly as a result of educational programs and public service campaigns. Movies and television shows depict complex yet competent people with mental illness, and a growing number of celebrities with depression are writing or speaking up about their own experiences.

Second, neuroscience research has established that mood regulation is a biological process. Depression is a result of interactions between the environment, life events, and brain function. In that sense, it is no different from any other medical illness. Ongoing efforts in both public awareness and brain and genetic research will, hopefully, continue to reduce the stigma of mental illness as people see that the mental and physical components of illness are intertwined.

Strength in numbers

Depression can be lonely not only for the person going through it, but also for family members. Because of the stigma surrounding depression, many people feel reluctant to talk about their feelings, concerns, and frustrations. As a result, it's easy to feel like you are the only one experiencing certain problems.

A good support group can help tear down walls of isolation. There you may find camaraderie and comfort in knowing that others understand what it's like to deal with mood problems.

A support group can also offer insight and help in dealing with common concerns. Support groups are often run by people who have been dealing with depression for decades, so you can benefit from their experience regarding health insurance issues, how to handle difficult situations, and other challenges. The other group members are also likely to offer helpful suggestions as well as encouragement.

Talking to others in your situation can infuse you with the energy you need to stick with your treatment or to encourage a family member to keep at it.

To find a support group near you, contact the National Alliance on Mental Illness at www.nami.org. The organization's website describes the different types of support groups available and can help you locate one in your area.

Navigating the health care system

Finding your way through the health care system isn't always easy. Many health insurance companies confine your choices to a narrow panel of doctors or therapists. And many psychiatrists, psychologists, and other mental health professionals do not accept insurance. You may choose to pay for services that the insurance company does not cover or pay out-of-pocket to see a therapist who does not take insurance. Dealing with that added financial burden can compound the stress you are already experiencing.

Most private insurers, Medicare, and managed care plans provide some coverage for mental health treatments. However, there may be a limit on how many visits the plan will cover, and copayments may be higher than for other types of care.

In 2008, the Mental Health Parity law required insurers to cover mental health treatments on a financial par with other health benefits, such as medical and surgical services. This law applies to employer-sponsored health plans, health coverage purchased through the Affordable Care Act, the Children's Health Insurance Program, and Medicaid. Medicare, however, is not subject to this law. And future legislation could either strengthen or weaken mental health coverage.

Even if you have access to providers and can pay for the care, making sure the different pieces of mental health treatment are coordinated properly can be another challenge. For example, more than one clinician may be involved in your treatment. You may need to keep your providers aware of the different parts of your care. The tips in "Making the health care system work for you" (above right) may prove helpful.

Making the health care system work for you

Dealing with health insurance matters and coordinating care is not easy even on your best day. But if you are depressed, sorting through financial and treatment issues can seem doubly difficult. Here are some things you can do to get the treatment you need more easily:

- Find out which mental health providers are covered by your insurance plan and ask if you have any coverage for doctors and therapists who are not in the network.
- Inquire about your health plan's mental health coverage and copayments, because out-of-pocket costs vary from insurer to insurer. If this seems overwhelming, ask a friend or family member to get the information for you.
- If a psychiatrist or doctor is prescribing your medication and another person is conducting psychotherapy, your treatment will be enhanced if you are all on the same page. Let both people know that you'd like them to communicate about your treatment and progress.
- Ask a supportive friend or family member to accompany you to an appointment both for moral support and to make sure you understand the recommended treatment.
- Take notes during your appointment so you can better understand information that may be confusing.
- Discuss any important and possibly time-consuming issues at the beginning of your appointment. Appointment time is often limited, so plan to make good use of the time.
- Make sure you have follow-up appointments for monitoring your treatment with your doctor.

Keeping mood symptoms at bay

In a memoir about living with bipolar disorder, Dr. Kay Redfield Jamison, a professor of psychiatry at Johns Hopkins University School of Medicine, wrote: "We all build internal sea walls to keep at bay the sadness of life and the often overwhelming forces within our minds." Her observation highlights a common challenge faced by people with mood disorders: learning how to manage fluctuating symptoms throughout life.

Practical advice on meeting this challenge comes from a study of 32 people with bipolar disorder who were functioning well (they had jobs and were living on their own). They identified a number of core strategies they used to avoid relapse and remain well. This is good advice for anyone with a mood disorder:

- Learn about your mood disorder and educate loved ones, to combat stigma.
- Get sufficient sleep and rest.
- Eat and exercise regularly.
- Monitor moods to be alert to early signs of relapse.
- Adhere to medication regimens, and increase doses as necessary.
- Practice yoga, tai chi, or other types of relaxing and meditative practices.

How to cope when a loved one is depressed, suicidal, or manic

Like a pebble thrown into a pond, depression, persistent depressive disorder, and bipolar disorder create ripples that spread far from their immediate point of impact. Those closest to people who have these illnesses often suffer alongside them. It's upsetting and often frustrating to deal with the inevitable fallout. But you can do a lot to help a loved one and yourself handle this difficult period.

Encourage him or her to get treatment and stick with it. Remind the person about taking medication or keeping therapy appointments.

Don't ignore comments about suicide. If you believe your loved one is suicidal, call his or her doctor or therapist. Mental health professionals can't divulge information about a patient without permission, but it is not a violation of confidentiality for them to listen to you. In urgent situations, if you can't reach the doctor or therapist, you may want to call a local crisis hotline for advice or bring the person to a local ER.

Care for yourself. Being a caregiver is a difficult job. You may want to seek individual therapy or join a support group. Numerous mental health organizations sponsor such groups and can also provide you with information on the illness and the latest treatments.

Offer emotional support. Your patience and love can make a huge difference. Ask questions and listen carefully to the answers. Try not to brush off or judge the other person's feelings, but do offer hope. Suggest activities that you can do together, and keep in mind that it takes time to get better. Don't worry if you don't know what to say—it takes a great deal of training (such as that received by therapists) to advise people in emotional distress.

Recognize that depression may manifest as irritability or anger, which is often directed toward family and other loved ones. Remind yourself that a disease is causing your loved one to act differently or perhaps be difficult. Do not blame him or her, just like you wouldn't if it were chronic physical pain that caused the person to change in certain ways.

Try to prevent reckless acts during manic episodes. It's all too common for a person to make poor decisions when manic, so it's a good idea to try to prevent this problem by limiting access to cars, credit cards, and bank accounts. Watch for signs that a manic episode is emerging. Disruption of sleep patterns can trigger an episode, so support your loved one in keeping a regular sleep schedule. Consistent patterns for other activities such as eating, exercising, and socializing may also help.

- Connect with others socially as much as you can.

Have a treatment plan ready so you know what to do when symptoms get worse. Enlist a loved one or friend who can help you implement the plan during a relapse, and keep that person informed about any changes in the plan.

Many participants said they kept trying different combinations of these specific strategies, and learned what helped through trial and error.

Tips to start (and stick to) your treatment plan

The following suggestions may help you clear some of the hurdles you may encounter on your journey to ease your depression:

- Ask a friend or family member to accompany you to your first appointment to help describe your problem, assist you in getting treatment, or simply offer support.
- Take medications as directed. Don't skip pills or change doses without consulting your doctor first.
- Report any side effects right away, and if necessary, talk to your doctor about adjusting your treatment plan.
- Set realistic goals for yourself. Try not to take on more than you can handle.
- Join in activities, and try not to isolate yourself from others. Depending on your personal preferences, attending religious services, joining a club, taking a class, having a meal with an understanding friend, or going to a movie, ball game, or concert may help lift your mood.
- Try to exercise regularly or take a daily walk.
- Hold off on making big decisions—about moving, changing jobs, getting married, or seeking a divorce—until your depression has eased or is under control.
- If you decide to try a "natural" remedy, such as SAMe, ask your doctor or pharmacist whether it might interact with any other medication you're taking.
- Friends and family often want to help. Let them. ■